Insights from friends

"There are those who have faced the black hole of cancer, and have been unable to positively face tomorrow. You are a testimony to what 'could be.' Your book will be a great resource for others. It is my hope they will receive comfort through the chapters, but more importantly, make a decision to face life day by day as a challenge as well as a positive influence in others' lives." *Chuck*

"I just finished reading with tears in my eyes. What a wonderful contribution you are making to help so many people who find themselves frightened and saddened; but with your book they are not alone." *Shula*

"Your family and friends have watched you 'fight the fight' with tremendous courage and determination. You will forever inspire so many of us who know you to never give up! Thank you for caring enough to help others." *Juli*

"'Joie de vivre' describes my good friend Michelle. Through her cancer diagnosis, many treatments, and long recovery, Michelle retained her sense of humor, her optimistic outlook, and her love of life. Her book will be educational, inspirational and comforting, to someone who is going through the cancer journey. Hopefully the reader will actually meet Michelle one day to benefit from the full amount of her wisdom and charisma." *Marlene*

from Cancer to Living

... a comprehensive and personal guide

Michelle Pardes

Still Breathing Publications
Dana Point, CA 92629

Still Breathing
From Cancer to Living
by Michelle Pardes

Published by Still Breathing Publications
Michelle Pardes
14 Monarch Bay Plaza, #135
Monarch Beach CA 92629
www.stillbreathing.org

ISBN: 978-1-4507-4530-7
Copyright © 2010 Michelle Pardes

Book Design and editing, Les is More Printing and Graphics
Author Photograph, Patrice Miller

Manufactured in the United States of America
10 9 8 7 6 5 4 3 2 1

To my husband Fred… The Supreme Saint,

my mother Suzanne… The Joyous Nurturer,

my sister Betty… The Dedicated Hero,

my brother-in-law Marty… The Caring Listener,

and to my father Julius… Spirit Mentor, in loving memory.

"The love of a family is life's greatest blessing"

Unknown

"We all live with the objective of being happy; our lives are all different and yet the same."

Anne Frank (1929-1945)

In the fall of 2003, I was diagnosed with blood cancer. Now I am a Graduate of The City of Hope Bone Marrow Transplant Class of 2004. According to my years of survivorship post transplant, as we go to press, I am a six year old. I am in the stage of wonderment, excited by all the new things I am learning. I wake up each day invigorated, excited with life, ready for new experiences, new people and new friends. I am no longer afraid of losing everything for I know I am able to adapt to my new situation and start all over again. My rebirth was made possible by the dedicated researchers and doctors at the City of Hope facility, in conjunction with Hoag Cancer Center, where options are offered, and dreams do come true.

Each year City of Hope hosts an annual event entitled "Celebration of Life Reunion." Bone marrow transplant survivors gather together at a grand barbecue. We are greeted by the caring medical team that saved our lives; they look at us in awe, telling us how amazing we now look. Survivors wear pins proclaiming the number of years of their survivorship. Speeches are delivered, we cheer for each other, and for the simple fact that we have lived another year.

At the end of the event, an aerial photograph is taken of all the bone marrow transplant survivors, gathered together. During the last photo shoot, I stood next to a survivor of 32 years. His picture, along with the aerial shot of other heroes, remains on my desk today.

During this reflective event, I always visit my room in the hospital where I was in isolation, to remind myself of how far I have come. Then I sit outside in the hospital's beautiful multicolored rose garden, and remember the weeks I spent incarcerated, longing for fresh air. I am always dazzled. Roses now signify for me the beauty of life, which I am able to be a part of because of those who dreamed the impossible can come true. I feel enormous gratitude. Without the amazing medical help of the doctors, researchers, nurses, nurse's aids, and technicians at City of Hope and Hoag Cancer Center, I wouldn't be alive today.

Chronologically, I am fifty-nine. I realize that although I fear the return of cancer again, I am resilient and love living. If I am again challenged by unwelcome cells in my body, I will again rise to the occasion and do battle.

I was once asked how someone like me, who appreciates living and life so much, could have cancer come knocking on her door. My response to that question was, why not me? I am no different than anyone else. But now I have a "bucket list" of things I want to accomplish each year of my survivorship.

My fifth year of survivorship, I decided to participate in The Team in Training Leukemia and Lymphoma Rock and Roll Marathon. I committed to walking a half marathon, 13.2 miles. I joined a team, trained, and promised to raise at least three thousand dollars for The Leukemia and Lymphoma Foundation.

My family was concerned over this commitment, but I was passionate. I will never forget the feeling of walking with so many people trying to bring an awareness of this dreaded disease. I marveled that five years before I could barely move, and now I was walking in a marathon.

And walk I did. I finished 13.2 miles in three hours and twenty four minutes. I raised fifteen thousand dollars, all donated by my generous supporters. I decided then that I would write a book, to make a difference in the lives of others who "walk in my shoes," experiencing the challenges of cancer. I wanted to help prepare them for the journey that lies ahead of them.

Upon starting this book I realized how very hard it is to capture this experience, trying to prepare someone for chemotherapy, radiation, doctor appointments, emotional upheavals. I wanted to prepare others for having "cancer."

Truthfully, there is no preparation for this journey. But I found that discussing my varied experiences and sharing what I've learned, allows others to become more familiar with what they might face. By writing this book, I am hoping to pave the way as a navigator, guide and coach for others challenged with cancer, and their loved ones. I will help you manage this doable journey. Paying it forward by helping those that are facing this trying battle is not only my mission, but my responsibility. I am here for you. You are not alone.

This poem by Forest Witcraft defines the purpose of my goal, I shared these words every year as a teacher.

> *"One Hundred Years from now*
> *It will not matter*
> *what kind of car I drove,*
> *what kind of house I lived in,*
> *how much money was in my bank account*
> *nor what my clothes looked like."*

What will be remembered is that you made a difference in the lives of others.

Good luck and take courage,

Michelle Pardes
aka Still Breathing...
Your Navigator and Survivorship Coach

INTRODUCTION

As I finished reading **Still Breathing** I felt moved by Michelle's authentic and powerful story. How dynamic, engaging, and zestful her journey! She provides a practical guide for going through the enormous challenges of a cancer patient, with simple, yet profound and eloquent road maps. With her use of inspiring quotations, she adds an uplifting spiritual aspect to surviving and thriving in the battle of her life.

When Michelle was diagnosed with Lymphoma, she learned to take control with courage and fortitude. She was determined and maintained humor, hope, and faith in her struggle to survive the same disease that killed her father, Julius Glantz. He served as a model of surviving for his daughter. A holocaust survivor, he modeled integrity, honesty, and passion with resilience. Michelle has carried his spirit with her allowing the fullness and richness of all experiences.

As a licensed therapist, I have facilitated support groups at The Wellness Community for 26 years, and continue to be inspired by Michelle and others who desperately fight for their lives.

With enormous courage to speak her truth, Michelle entered The Wellness Community 7 years ago. She became a member of a cancer support group, joining with others in their fight for recovery. I was impressed immediately with her intensity and determination to fight the good fight on this journey. With her courage to do "whatever it takes," she learned the ropes from veteran members and contributed her own intuitive wisdom to the weary band of fellow travelers. (In 2009, The Wellness Community and Gilda's House merged, creating the Cancer Support Network, the largest cancer support group worldwide.)

Still Breathing is Michelle's gift to those who are stunned with a diagnosis of cancer. She is paying it forward with her expert guidance and coaching. Michelle's extraordinary chutzpah, joi de vivre, and experience of the challenges, make her a natural guide. She yearns to empower others with her enthusiasm, encouragement, wisdom and soul.

Now, survival with a new normal and looking at life with new eyes is the challenge. How to live with the uncertainty of life and the fear of recurrence, while being in the present moment to enjoy?

Michelle has shared that thought, and assures herself that if cancer returns, she can and will fight again and be a victor again.

I am eternally grateful for the privilege and the pleasure of accompanying my dear Michelle on our shared journey of laughter, tears, sorrow, joy and celebration of life with the richness and fullness of it all.

With respect and love,
Sandra Weiss, PhD

ITINERARY

"The long and winding road"

The Beatles

CHAPTER 1

DISCOVERING "THE LUMP"

"Abolish fear and you can accomplish whatever you wish"

Elbert Hubbard

My discovery of this alien object happened on May 29, 2003. I was dismissing my class, running to attend a meeting. I knew I looked disheveled, as I always did at the end of a teaching day. Trying to quickly straighten up, I fixed my hair and arranged the scarf I had around my neck. It was then I felt it.

The Lump. A feeling of dread came over me. I stopped walking. I couldn't move. I kept feeling this large, protruding growth over and over again. I entered a surreal state of mind.

A teacher friend of mine was walking towards me. All I could manage to say is that I have this lump. She looked at my face, which had the look of horror, and promptly dispelled any reason why I should be scared of the silly little thing on the left side of my neck. She sited so many stories as to when she'd had swollen glands, yet I didn't hear one word she said.

I was able to get hold of myself, put on a professional face, and proceeded to enter the meeting room. I was to participate in a Child Study Meeting; a collaborative educational team that meets to discuss the special needs of individual students. (At specific times parents of the child discussed are asked to attend). As I entered the room, looking at the team sitting around the table, including the parents of a student who happened to be in my classroom, I miraculously forgot about the uninvited guest that had lodged itself on my neck.

The meeting took approximately two hours. As everyone started to exit the room, my fears and apprehension re-entered. I knew I had to call the one person who would first calm me down, and then direct me as to what I should do, my sister Betty. Betty was a Nurse Practitioner at an office in Irvine, about 35 minutes away from my school. I made the call. Being that this was the Friday before Memorial Day, most of her staff was leaving for the long weekend. However, she managed to have one doctor stay until I got to her office.

Needless to say, my ability to speak coherently literally stopped. All I could say to my sister, and then the doctor I saw, is "Oh my God, I have a lump." I also reacted as I think any person would react in my situation with the family history I have, I jumped to conclusions, convinced I had "The Big C" and that I was going to die within the next minute or two.

After being calmed down, with the reassurance that we would know more after the blood test results were read, I started to almost breathe again, although still frightened.

The weekend my lump was discovered was appropriately called "Memorial Weekend." Sitting on the table in the examining room, I started reflecting about how a similar lump came as an uninvited guest to someone I treasured so dearly, my father. Twenty-five years ago, my father was diagnosed with Chronic Lymphocytic Leukemia; BLOOD CANCER.

Deja Vu.

TRAVEL GUIDE TIPS

• *You are NOT a doctor, therefore wait, do NOT investigate, or speculate until you have your next appointment. By then, you will have listened to your body, and if necessary, flagged any other symptoms that you might find out of the ordinary.*

• *Being dishonest about the symptoms you are experiencing can only hurt you and not help your cause in getting to the bottom of your medical mystery. You may want to ignore important signs that are presented to you, however, what you ignore, doesn't necessarily ignore you. Tell your doctor.*

• *Do not compare yourself to those you know who had similar symptoms. Their circumstances might have been totally different.*

• *Surround yourself with those who you love. Fill your days with "Happy Moments" and positive energy.*

• *Implement mind and body techniques in order to stay calm, i.e. yoga, walks on the beach, listening to music, watch a movie (nothing related to medical dramas) that you know will engage you.*

CHAPTER 2

THE IMPOSSIBLE DIAGNOSIS

"Doubt is the hell in the human soul"

Comtesse Catherine de Gasparin

I was diagnosed by the doctor Betty worked for: I had mononucleosis. Needless to say, not only was I extremely shaken up being told that I had mono, I was frustrated - I was told I had to have bed rest, curtail my activities, and be off from school for two weeks. I could not process, nor did I want to understand, the concept of sitting still or being "unproductive." Besides, I was then under the impression that I was not expendable, and that I was the only one who could get the job done in my classroom. I was needed by my students.

Learning to sit, rest, sleep, and eat slowly, was new to me. I was so used to being a "multi-tasker," juggling my family activities, my professional life, my committee meetings, my sport activities. The concept of focusing on myself was truly foreign to me.

What I didn't realize was that my body didn't care what I was mentally used to, physiologically, the command that my brain was giving was to sleep non stop. I had very little appetite. I also started experiencing severe leg and stomach pains. At night I was profusely sweating, going through at least three to four pairs of pajamas a night.

I chose to remain silent regarding these symptoms. At first I attributed them to my diagnosis of mono. However, deep inside my subconscious, I knew that my body systems were off. I was in deep denial, a place that did feel comfortable to me for fleeting moments. But I couldn't stop my curious nature. I started being a medical investigator and began my own search into a world that was totally unfamiliar to me.

The more I researched and read, using both the internet, and when I was feeling well enough, medical books from every local book store imaginable, the more I learned that my diagnosis was impossible. I could not find one person whom at 52 years old had been diagnosed with mononucleosis. The oldest person I found with this infectious disease was 38 years old. This is not to say that the results of my blood test were wrong, I definitely showed a positive result for having mono, however, the occurrence of this illness could have happened many years before.

Mononucleosis, so lovingly called "The Kissing Disease," is evident in a much younger population, generally college age students. Their busy schedules and active social lives put them at risk of infection.

I acknowledge that I was always running around to an excessive degree, but I certainly was not engaged in "loving exchanges" with anyone except for my husband. I showed my students affection by giving them "Mrs. Pardes' happy hugs." Based upon all the research I did for weeks (I was obsessed), I came to the conclusion that I COULD NOT HAVE MONONUCLEOSIS!

During that time, I kept thinking of my father. I did research on the internet, and based upon what I was reading, there was no genetic link in the area of blood cancers. Somehow that didn't make me feel comfortable with the fact that my physiological symptoms were very much like my father's.

As time progressed, I was convinced that I could reduce the swelling of my lymph nodes by going to get them drained. A medical therapist was recommended to me who's area of expertise was lymphatic drainage (she was not a licensed doctor).

I really liked going to this therapist, she had a positive attitude and was convinced that I did not have cancer. She felt my symptoms were in direct correlation to my being stressed due to a busy and chaotic family life, and not getting enough rest. She placed me on supplements to boost my energy.

I was convinced that I was feeling better, had more energy, and my night sweats were dissipating. I also convinced myself that my lump was shrinking. It is truly shocking how one can be in such denial.

Luckily, Betty never gave up being convinced that my illness was serious. She made sure that I was going to her office for blood checks every two weeks. What I didn't know at the time was that she was researching continually as to the unusual presentation of certain results on my blood panels called eosinophils. She learned that elevated eosinophils were an indicator of lymphoma, which she suspected I had.

At the beginning of July, just prior to Independence Day, and our leaving for a visit to Oregon to see my brother and sister-in-law, Betty insisted I have a needle biopsy of my enlarged lymph. Needless to say I was not on board to do this. After all, I only had mono. Why did I have to bother with this test? I was feeling better, my lump was going down, and nothing was wrong with me.

After much convincing that this test was in my best interest, and that Betty just wanted to confirm the mono diagnosis, I agreed to have the biopsy.

Entering the Ear, Nose and Throat Specialist's office made me highly anxious. I was so ready to put this illness behind me that I did not want to talk about the possibilities of different illnesses. Seeing the doctor take out this huge needle that he was going to insert into the lump in my neck nearly made me jump out of my skin. Yet somehow, I managed to get through it.

That test was my first introduction to "Test Anxiety." There is nothing worst than waiting for test results. The doctor told me that the results would not be in until the Monday after the July 4th weekend.

There was nothing to do but get on the plane to Oregon and try to enjoy myself. I was immersed in thinking that I was seriously ill, and speculated what would I do if it was cancer. My family and friends were most kind and patient with me, trying to side-track and entertain me through my "what if" moments.

You can't stop time, and Monday did arrive. My sister promised me that she would be at the Ear, Nose and Throat doctor's office exactly at their opening time to check on the results (she worked in the same building as the ENT doctor).

I was pacing by my sister-in-law's phone. I couldn't stop moving. My husband and brother-in-law went for a walk. They figured the phone call would happen no matter what, and staying inside next to me wouldn't expedite it. My husband, Fred, was convinced that there was nothing really big wrong with me and that I was worrying about nothing. After all, doctors know what they are talking about.

Fifteen minutes after they left, with 5 mg. of Valium in me (I was having a major anxiety episode, but luckily I had been given a prescription for this), I received the phone call from the doctor. He told me that my results were benign. Betty called me immediately after the doctor did, confirming that the results of the needle biopsy were benign.

Saying I breathed a sigh of relief is an understatement. I felt like I had been reborn. My death sentence had been lifted, I thought now I could live again without ever seeing any more doctors. I called Fred to come home from his walk, and the four of us had a wonderful celebration. I remember the smiles on all our faces when we ate out that night at a lovely beachside restaurant. We later went to see the fire works at Cannon Beach. Somehow that night the fireworks seemed more beautiful than I had ever remembered them to be!

TRAVEL GUIDE TIPS

• *If you feel that things are just "not right" with your body, and your symptoms are still presenting themselves despite test results, seek help from knowledgeable specialists who are more familiar with the illness you might think you have.*

• *Make sure that the diagnostic procedures used are appropriate measures for what the medical professionals suspect is wrong. Ask questions.*

• *Knowledge is Power! The more you know the better your chances are to have the necessary intervention to solve your problem. Keeping yourself uninformed is denial, hiding your symptoms is denial. The only one you are lying to is yourself.*

• *Remember no matter what the diagnosis might be, no matter what measures you have to take to be "Still Breathing," you have the strength to face the medical options that will bring you future health and happiness!*

CHAPTER 3

IT'S SHOW AND TELL TIME

"Just go out there and do what you've got to do."

Martina Navratilova

No matter what my body was doing to me, creating physical and emotional havoc, I was focused on what I considered my priorities at the time. I had many different goals and objectives that had to be addressed.

First and foremost, my daughter was getting married in December. Jennifer was living in Vermont, and her twin brother David was going for his Masters in Business at Boston University. Jennifer and I decided to meet in Boston, along with my mother, to purchase her wedding gown. It was essential to me to have this bonding experience with my daughter, and nothing was going to stop me!

Something so wonderful, so exciting, was so unbearable for me. I remember getting off the plane, and each step I took I felt that I was going to collapse. My face was beet red, I was drenched in sweat, and my breathing was labored. The lump on my neck began to pull and started to burn. Yet, I marched on, driven to achieve a most important goal, to help my daughter purchase the dress of her dreams.

My mother – daughter time did not go as I had planned. While Jennifer was searching through the racks filled with wedding gowns, all I could think of was that I was going down quickly. Those three hours were so difficult for me. I will never forget the kindness of the strangers I met at the bridal salon. They must have sensed something was wrong and so graciously helped my daughter into the gown she purchased, along with finding her veil and other things that were needed for her wedding. Sitting there watching how beautiful my daughter looked in her gown, I knew that no matter what I was going to be at her wedding.

After accomplishing what I had set out to do with Jennifer, I was able to explore Boston with my son David, and his girlfriend Liz (they are now happily married, and have a beautiful young son). David was confused, for everywhere I went by foot, I lagged behind. I couldn't walk and keep up with him. I even asked for cabs for such short distances of one city block. Here, his active Mom, who was even a tennis player, was incapable of moving easily. I made up some excuse as to why I was acting so strangely.

That trip back east became even more stressful for I continued my travels with my mom to Vermont, along with Jennifer and her fiancé Andy (now her husband, with a lovely four year old son). I remember each time the car went over a simple bump I could have screamed in pain, and yet I continued to smile).

My mother, Suzanne, the adventurer she is, and I even went to Montreal, Canada, from Vermont, by bus. I couldn't wait to see the countryside. But the only thing I saw was darkness. I couldn't keep my eyes open. Again, I told my mom that I was just tired because of thinking about the plans for the wedding and going back to school.

It is amazing what one does to try to take care of themselves just to get relief from one second of unbearable pain. I was waking up at 5:00 in the morning at the hotel we were staying in, so I could sneak down to the pool where the water was ice cold. I soaked my legs, thinking that the cold water would numb my severe bone aches.

We stayed in Montreal, Canada for three days. Each step I took while sightseeing was unbearable. The grimaces on my face may have looked like smiles, but I was really gritting my teeth.

My mother and I had a few things on our agenda during this trip. Mom wanted to see her first cousin whom she was very close to. Fortunately the cousin showed us around town via car. I would have never been able to do a "walking tour."

My cousin, Leo, was equally excited about my Jennifer's upcoming wedding, and insisted on taking us to the discount Wedding Attire Section in Montreal. I couldn't refuse him for I didn't want to remove his feeling of joy (he, too, like my mother, was a Holocaust Survivor. He and his sister were the last children put on the Kinder Transport from Gratz, Austria and taken to Israel via boat. They never saw their parents again).

We went from store to store, looking for a "Mother of the Bride Dress" in periwinkle, a difficult color to find (ultimately, my daughter agreed to let the mothers of both bride and groom to wear black). The temperature was hot that day, yet I was freezing. I made an excuse that I was catching a cold so I could run in a store to purchase a wrap.

After shopping, I was beyond exhausted. My bones ached internally. My cousin and mother were hungry and we stopped for lunch at a very famous delicatessen which specialized in pastrami.

The last thing I wanted to do was eat. All I wanted to do was take an ice bath to numb my pain. Once again, not wanting to be rude, I accommodated my traveling companions. I don't know how I made it through that lunch. The crowds in the restaurant were overwhelming, the smell of pastrami was offensive to me (I was extremely sensitive to the smell of greasy foods). I faked eating some, and by the time I went back to the hotel I was near collapse.

On our return trip, my mom began to realize there was something very wrong with me. I had a temperature in the airport, and despite the hot tea she purchased for me, I couldn't get warm. Her look of worry was one that is forever imprinted in my brain. I knew then, no matter what the outcome would be, I would have to find out what was wrong with me.

My promise regarding my health was short lived. I got home, got back involved in setting up my classroom, and organizing the wedding. I still don't know how I physically managed. Each time I had to enter or exit my car, I winced in pain, moving extremely slowly.

My sister watched me like a hawk, constantly feeling my lump. She accused me of losing weight (can you imagine that? I had dieted all my life, dreaming of being able to eat anything I wanted, and the weight was flying off of me, I had lost almost twenty pounds when I turned 52 years old, what a birthday gift!).

Being the actress I am, I had also convinced my very close friends that there was nothing wrong with me. I never disclosed the many unusual symptoms I was experiencing to them. They felt that Betty was being overly cautious.

In retrospect, I did suspect there was something very wrong with me. But I was able to use all my daily distractions as avoidance. I stuck my head in the sand, willing myself to just not think that I could be very sick.

My sister continued checking my blood levels every few weeks. Being the thorough detective and diagnostician she is, she noted that my eosinophils were elevated. She knew from nightly visits to her computer that the elevated eosinophils were an indicator that I did not have mono. A positive mono-stat test does not necessarily mean you are presently ill with this infectious disease. It could also mean you had mono in past years.

Betty knew my visible symptoms (my lump still existed, never shrinking), along with the readings of my blood test, were a possible indicator that I had lymphoma. She was determined to get me to the appropriate specialist who would further investigate what she was suspicious of, that I had Non-Hodgkin Lymphoma, cancer of the immune system (lymph nodes, white blood cells and plasma).

There are times when you know you are being manipulated because are unable to make a decision that is right for yourself. Deep down inside, instinctively, you know you have to make the right choice, to learn what the truth is. I trusted Betty with my life and knew that she would guide me and point me in the right direction.

Betty wrote to the same infectious disease doctor that had diagnosed my father years earlier. She stated in the letter that I was being stubborn, and was reluctant to go on with further medical investigation. My sister then spoke to me, convincing me that this particular doctor would help me monitor my infectious disease (mono) and apply the necessary interventions to help me feel better.

When I entered this particular doctor's office, one that I had been to so many times before with my father, I started to relax thinking that I was in good shape and would feel better soon. I also knew that the doctor I was seeing was extremely kind, and he would not say anything to upset me.

Nothing like being delusional.

In my past encounters with this doctor, he always greeted me with such warmth, a smile and hug.

This time his behavior towards me was extremely different. He looked gravely at me, no smile, stating that I must have a biopsy of the enlarged node on the left side of my neck immediately. At that point in our visit, I started to hyperventilate, begging him to tell me that everything was okay, and that I would be just fine. He couldn't do that. He arranged for my biopsy the very next day.

From the time of my doctor's visit to the time when I had the biopsy, I was numb. I still couldn't believe that anything was that seriously wrong with me. I even told the doctors in the biopsy operating room that I would give them each a bottle of wine if they could find nothing wrong with me.

WAITING FOR TEST RESULTS AGAIN.

I knew it would take about a day to hear the results. Each minute felt like a year. Somehow I managed to go to work, immersing myself in my passion, teaching children.

At noon the day after my biopsy, the phone rang in my classroom. I somehow knew that the news was not going to be good. The doctor confirmed what I really had suspected, my biopsy was positive. I had CANCER. I immediately called the vice principal to come to my classroom so I could privately call my husband and tell him the news.

I remember seeing my students' eyes growing larger, looking fearfully at me when I returned back to the classroom. Their feelings were my number one priority, for I would never want to traumatize them.

It was my job, my responsibility, to act as normally as I could. I had been through many traumatic events, like September 11th, while teaching my students. You must keep your students calm. Their reactions reflect your reactions.

I told my students that I had a family situation that I had to tend to, and that I would see them tomorrow. The beauty of children is that they trust what they see and hear. I acted calmly, giving them no reason to worry. I also told them that after lunch they were having a special movie treat. They were to go to another second grade classroom with their things. The other teacher would dismiss them.

How I drove my car after I left my classroom is a mystery to me. It felt like I was having an out of body experience. Nothing felt real. The body is an amazing machine, having the right built-ins to handle the crisis you are facing. All I knew is that I had to get to my brother-in-law's house which was over five miles away. My mother, who I had also telephoned with my news, was going to his house to meet me, comfort me and help me decide on my next course of action.

HOW LUCKY I AM TO HAVE THE FAMILY I DO!

There is nothing greater than belonging to your family tribe. Each member, loving you, supporting you and helping handle the most unimaginably difficult situation makes you feel blessed and so fortunate. My brother-in-law, with his ability to make me laugh even in the most grim situations, and my mother, who was supremely focused and grounded, went into action.

We contacted my mother's best friend and our family's guardian angel, who at the time was in France. He was a knowledgeable and respected physician at Hoag Hospital whom I trusted implicitly. He recommended two oncologists that were highly experienced with blood cancers (ironically he had been equally helpful with my father when he had cancer, fortuitously introducing him to Dr. Levine, who later on becomes significant in my survivorship). We immediately called the two oncologists that we were referred to...AND MY JOURNEY BEGAN.

No matter what may happen to you in one minute, no matter how big the crisis may be, there are still your priorities that supersede everything else. I had an appointment at the bakery later that afternoon with my daughter's wedding planner, a wonderful friend of mine, to order my daughter's and future son-in-law's wedding cake. Yes, I made the appointment.

Can you imagine in the midst of being told I had cancer, I went on to a cake tasting, discussing very important cake topics, how many layers you want in the cake, what flavor each layer should be, and what frosting would you like? Again, I felt that everything was surreal, yet, I knew this was my new reality. I also knew that no matter what danger I was facing, LIFE MUST GO ON!

TRAVEL GUIDE TIPS

• *Don't bite off more than you can chew. Allow yourself time to process something so BIG.*

• *Allow yourself to react to your predicament. It is OKAY to scream, cry, jump up and down. Do whatever it takes to help you feel better.*

• *Lean on your loved ones. Remember no matter what they say, they are only trying to make you feel better. They feel scared and helpless too.*

• *Limit your research. You have enough on your plate just handling the change you are about to face. Remember that even though the change was not what you wanted, you are going to have so many unbelievable experiences, you will have opportunities to learn more about who you are, and also meet HEROES along your journey.*

• *Remember that as we grow, change is inevitable. We all face "The Big C", CHALLENGE. Your present challenge just happens to come in the form of cancer. You have what it takes to manage this crisis, for since you were born, we all learned to walk despite how many times we fell down.*

CHAPTER 4

SEEING A NEW WORLD

"Always behave like a duck, keep calm and unruffled on the surface, but paddle like the devil underneath"

Lord Barbizon

"Lights, Cameras, Action – It Is Show Time."

The job I had ahead of me the day after my cancer diagnosis was going to be a huge challenge. As a teacher, no matter what your plans are, you have to expect the unexpected. I did know it was going to take an Academy Award performance to convince my sweet and innocent students that Mrs. Pardes was just going to have to leave for a short while, and would be fine.

Fortunately, the week of my diagnosis was Red Ribbon Week. Students were being taught to say NO TO DRUGS. I designed a lesson regarding the difference between drugs that can hurt you and good drugs that can make you feel better when you are sick. I somehow managed to be extremely upbeat in explaining that I needed to have "the good drugs" in order to help me feel better for I wasn't feeling well. The students were luckily engaged in the lesson, never realizing how truly terrified I was.

The day went extremely quickly. I remember trying to get all my curriculum in order for my long term substitute, not even knowing how to plan for I didn't know how long my absence would be.

The school community that I worked in was extremely close. News spread quickly regarding my unexpected medical situation. So many parents showed up at my door when I was dismissing my students, some crying, some had flowers, all had the look of concern and shock. I also had a visit from a "true angel," a parent from our school community who had been ill with lymphoma, and went through so much including a bone marrow transplant. She was so comforting to me, sharing what I would be facing and reassuring me that I would be okay.

I truly don't know how I kept my emotions under control saying good-bye. Being surrounded by that loving support helped make such a difference in the day that was so enormously difficult for me. Leaving was one of the hardest things I ever had to do in my life!

I had an appointment with a highly recommended oncologist the next day, Dr. Louis Vandermoelen (whom I still see today). He welcomed me with kind eyes, and a strong hand shake that exuded confidence. I felt I could trust him immediately.

My mother, my sister and my husband all came with me for the initial visit. Luckily our mood was not too bad for we thought that all I needed was some chemotherapy, and I would be back to normal in no time. Little did I know what was in store for me.

Dr. Vandermoelen did not know that as of yet no one had spoken to me about what lymphoma is and what was needed to further stage my illness. He also did not realize that no one had spoken to me regarding the protocol I needed to have ASAP in order to put my cancer into remission.

Upon entering the examination room, where only my sister was allowed with me, the oncologist began to talk about what chemotherapy I needed and its side effects. He advised that I should have CHOP; Cytoxan, Adriamycin or Hydroxydaunomycin, Vincristine or Oncovin, and Prednisone. This was the highly recommended protocol for the cancer that I had.

During his discussion with me, my sister Betty noticed I had grown pale, and I was breathing heavily. She stopped the oncologist, immediately saying PLEASE STOP AND EXPLAIN WHAT IS HAPPENING. No one had told me yet what I was facing.

Dr. Vandermoelen was most understanding and accommodating. He began to explain about the chemotherapy I was going to receive, how often I was going to have the infusions, and the possible side effects I would experience. When he started to talk about hair loss, I couldn't process anything else he was saying.

I felt like I was going to faint. All of a sudden, I heard this large scream. I didn't realize that horrible, guttural, human scream was mine. That one loud howl expressed the shock, the pain I was feeling. The fact I was going to lose my hair was too much for me to bare.

I was about to face the unimaginable. I had always treasured my hair. I felt that part of my body defined me.

Then I suddenly realized that my daughter's wedding was going to be in six weeks. The thought that I was going to be bald for my daughter's wedding was inconceivable to me.

I felt so light headed. I collapsed into my sister's arms, sobbing, makeup dripping all over her shirt. My life as I knew it was never going to be the same.

The realization that I had cancer finally sank in. That one phone call from the surgeon, along with hearing the oncologist describe my cancer and what I had to do in order to try to get my health back, was going to totally turn my world upside down.

When you think that your present situation can't get any worse than it is, you are proven wrong. It can get even more difficult than you know.

In order to assess the progression of my cancer, the oncologist needed to perform a bone marrow tap, the aspiration of my bone marrow. Emotional pain is one thing, but experiencing the worst physical pain has its own category.

I was first given a drug called Versed in order to help put me in a trance like state. This sedation is supposed to help alleviate the painful injection needed to remove your marrow from the bone.

However, even though I was sedated, I still felt an indescribable pain in my hip and traveling down my leg. Then I heard the sounds of the needle penetrating my bones. I also heard a loud scraping sound, as if a large bird, a hawk, was piercing my bone happily picking, poking and prodding. I was his newly discovered prey.

It felt like I was being crucified alive. What must have been a matter of minutes, felt like hours, if not days. I never thought I would live to see the end of those moments.

I later learned that my family, sitting in the waiting room adjacent to the exam room where I was having this procedure, heard my screams and pleas for the doctor to stop. They had no idea what I was going through and experiencing.

Throughout this traumatic day and new medical experience, I thought I had a handle on my new reality. In retrospect I really had no idea of what my future challenging journey might have in store for me.

I only knew one thing I could hold on to, to maintain my focus of what was real and important to me. I wanted more than anything to be alive and see my daughter get married.

TRAVEL GUIDE TIPS

• *Try to learn about necessary diagnostic procedures and the level of pain you might experience. If the doctors and medical personnel tell you a procedure can cause pain, investigate alternative ways of going about this diagnostic path. Ask if it is possible for you to be placed in "twilight sleep" where you not only feel no pain, you have no memory of this experience.*

• *Rome was not built in one day, you can't expect a solution and result in one day. Hold on to the daily goal of having good health. No pain, no gain.*

• *Trust yourself, it is about you and how you choose to handle your intervention. Don't force yourself to do things that are not feeling comfortable to you. If you need to go into "turtle mode," cover yourself with blankets and remain solo, give yourself permission to do so. Conserve your energy. It can be exhausting trying to have conversations, continually answering the same questions, or repeatedly saying you are doing fine when you don't feel it.*

• *Stop feeling unproductive during your recuperation. You are actually being HUGELY productive for you are actively fighting and doing battle against cancer cells.*

• *Balance the obligations you have on your plate. If you are faced with a large obligation, for example a wedding, ask for help. Being involved with commitments you made prior to your illness can be a great distraction.*

CHAPTER 5

CRASHES

"Humpty Dumpty sat on the wall,
Humpty Dumpty had a great fall,
All the king's horses,
And all the king's men,
Couldn't put Humpty Dumpty together again"

Nursery Rhyme

It seems that every time I am personally involved with weddings, drama appears in one form or another. At my own wedding over thirty five years ago, an unforgettable and totally unexpected Pardes event happened.

After the world's longest engagement, over 17 months, our very planned wedding took place. Our wedding vows were exchanged under a traditional Chuppah; a wedding canopy. The top of our covering was an array of beautiful white flowers. The covering was held up by four Grecian pillars, one at each corner. To the side of the groom stood his parents, to my side stood my parents.

At the end of a Jewish wedding, the groom breaks a glass, signifying the destruction of the Temple in Jerusalem many years ago (another interpretation of the breaking of the glass is that it is the last time the groom gets to put his foot down and have his say). Then, the groom kisses the bride, and the guests break out into loud cheers, singing heartfelt Mazel Tovs (congratulations).

That happy wedding ending did not happen for us. We did not experience that story book ending.

After my husband broke the glass, and I lifted my head to receive his kiss (he is one foot taller than I am), instead of hearing Mazel Tov I heard loud screams. Simultaneous to the loud screams I felt Fred pull me out of the Chuppah.

My father-in-law had experienced a hyperglycemic attack where his blood sugar levels plummeted. At the time of our kiss, he had fainted, knocking over the pillar that he was leaning on. My mother, as short as I am, attempted to hold up her side of the pillar, trying to prevent the whole canopy from falling. Unfortunately, she was unsuccessful.

There was sheer bedlam. My mother-in-law was bent over her husband, who was unconscious at the time, screaming for help. Our wedding guests were in shock. People ran to get help. They called for an ambulance which arrived promptly, along with police and fire engines.

My new husband, who did rescue me from the falling canopy, took my hand and walked me upstairs to the Bridal Salon for I was hysterical. I became ill and had to visit the bathroom.

When I emerged from the bathroom, the officiating Rabbi tried to cheer me up. He rationalized that this occurrence would mean that in our future as a married couple, we would be doubly blessed in life. We certainly were, for four years later we had boy and girl twins.

Flash forward: now I was seeing my daughter get married, and it was even more meaningful due to the circumstances that I was in. I wanted everything to go just perfectly.

However, the usual wedding mishaps did take place, luckily on the humorous side. For example, when I arrived at The Laguna Cliffs Marriott to pick up the women of the immediate family to get their hair done, we witnessed something else entirely get done!

There was an Indian wedding at the hotel prior to our wedding party. In Indian ceremonies, it is customary to have the new young couple ride horseback into their event. As we pulled up, two beautiful white stallions were standing in front of the hotel, waiting to be mounted by the groom and bride. Unfortunately, nature called, the horses did their "business" right in front of our car, where my daughter was sitting! It didn't bode well for her or anyone else within close proximity to the stallions. We were certainly appreciative that horses are not used for Jewish weddings.

Aside from other small crises that occurred (like having the lingering smell of curry throughout the hallways of the Marriott due to the previous wedding) all went beautifully.

I remember walking my daughter down the aisle with her father, thinking in amazement that I made it. My dream was coming true. I was able to see the joy on Jennifer's face as she entered under the wedding canopy and was greeted by her groom (this time the canopy remained standing). That moment in time will stay with me forever.

During the festivities, I felt like I was on top of the world, dancing the night away. It was hardly believable that I had six rounds of chemotherapy in me, and I had a full head of hair (my hair DID NOT FALL OUT. I thought that was a miracle in itself...the percentages worked in my favor regarding chances of losing the hair with the chemotherapy I picked). I was dancing non-stop. My adrenaline was flowing, and no one could believe that I was sick. I looked too good.

However, what goes up, must come down. I certainly did do that, and I went down hard. From one moment to the next I was filled with exhilaration and went to desperation, for I couldn't catch my breath, I couldn't breathe.

The day after the wedding, Jennifer's husband's parents hosted a brunch at the hotel. I had noticed that my chest was tightening, and I had pains in that area. I was too busy still feeling the joy of the night before, and I totally ignored my symptoms. By nightfall, it tightened up even more, and I was gasping for air.

Stubborn as I am, I knew the next day I would have to have my chest checked. Luckily, my daughter, son-in-law, and most out of town wedding guests (people came from all parts of the world to celebrated this most joyous event; Israel, France, Egypt, New York, Canada, North Carolina, Philadelphia, San Francisco, Florida, Oregon, etc.) left. It was time for me to apprise Fred we needed to go to the hospital for a chest x-ray. I had called my oncologist discreetly so as not to alarm anyone.

Life is so unpredictable. One minute you are in a chair in the air, with everyone dancing the hora around you, and then the next minute you are driving with your husband down Pacific Coast Highway, gasping for air.

I had an eerie premonition entering Hoag Hospital. I felt like something was not going right, yet I was so grateful I had made it to the wedding (yes, on time too).

The doctor who took the chest x-ray looked concerned when he heard me cough. He did know my medical history and told me that my oncologist would call me immediately when they got the results.

Driving back home, I was looking at the ocean, wondering what my medical future held. I had not really experienced any side effects. I naively thought this chemotherapy is a piece of cake. Little did I know what I was in store for.

Fred's phone rang when we were just 10 minutes from home. It was my oncologist telling my husband I had to return to the hospital immediately, that I had Pneumocystis Pneumonia. I needed immediate intervention.

I was so close to home, I begged Fred to allow me to pack, I wanted to take clean underwear, a robe and other personal items. I felt so deflated when I returned home to gather my things. My friends were there with my older son, all were having so much fun. Yet, here I was, about to experience one of the many times I would be yanked out of the mainstream of my everyday life.

Despite this crisis, I still had some of my wits about me. I knew that when a person goes to a hospital, it is best not to take any of their personal jewelry. Just before leaving home for the hospital, I went back into my bedroom, took off all my jewelry, placed it into a sock, and then put the sock into my underwear drawer. I even told my friend just in case I had a lapse in my memory, to remind me where I hid my treasures, many having sentimental value to me.

Driving back down PCH, going back to the hospital within two hours of leaving there, I felt emotionally numb. I was in a trance state when they put me in a room, placed oxygen immediately over my face, started my IV, and put the oxygen monitor over my index finger.

Over the next few days, I was in and out of consciousness. I was having severe bouts of coughing with major difficulties in breathing. I was given heavy dosages of steroids (that was my first introduction to the "Evil Drug") and Bactrim; a strong antibiotic that leaves horrible side effects in your mouth.

"Please let me be, no more poking me, let me alone," are unrealistic desires when you are hospitalized. You become nocturnal, not knowing whether it is day or night. You also have invasive procedures, where if you're lucky, you are asleep, feeling nothing. However, when I had the experience of them placing lines down my nostrils, I felt everything, I was sure I was going to choke to death.

I was to remain in the hospital for two weeks. I knew that I had to get myself ambulatory, I had to walk and exercise my lungs. Easier said than done. To take just one step, in my weakened condition, was quite a challenge. Yet, step by step, I eventually was able to walk down a hospital hallway without stopping.

As Dorothy said in the Wizard of Oz, "I just want to go home," that is all I wanted to do, just go home.

That finally became possible exactly two weeks after the wedding.

There is certainly truth to the statement that you can never go home again, nothing ever is the same. My house no longer felt familiar to me. I remember asking my husband, is the house neat, are the newspapers put away? Bless his little heart, for according to his "clean house value system," the house looked perfect.

My "clean house value system" has totally different criteria. Entering my home for the first time, even if I had relaxed my criteria, I could never have imagined that no one noticed the wedding flowers all over the house, THE VERY DEAD WEDDING FLOWERS, that I had spent hours reviewing and ordering.

Sudden sadness enveloped me. I felt so weak, and totally empty. Nothing made sense to me. Little did I know that the steroids I was given were creating havoc with my brain cells. High dosages of that drug truly change your personality. I retreated to bed, making a promise that the next day, I would call my beloved cleaning lady of over 20 years. I needed to have order back. I needed to feel in control again.

Waking up in my own bed, without being awakened in the middle of the night to be weighed and have my blood pressure taken, was wonderful. After my cup of coffee, I called my cleaning lady. She happily arrived within a few hours, and she and her crew made me feel like Cinderella. They turned my house into my precious castle, looking sparkly and clean.

After they left, I still felt like something else was missing. I realized that I had none of my rings on my fingers. I remembered where I had placed my rings, and went into my drawer to get the sock bag where I had placed my jewelry.

I went into my underwear drawer, went towards the right side where I placed the sock bag, and nothing was there. I retried that spot again. Once again, I couldn't find the bag. My emotional level went from calmness to hysteria in a matter of minutes. I emptied every single drawer in my dresser, and no sock bag...there was nothing.

I started hyperventilating, barely able to reach for the phone to call Fred for I was sure we were robbed (steroids can also make you hyper-emotional and paranoiac). When I finally reached him, I shrieked we need to call the police, we have been robbed.

Yes, I did jump to conclusions, however I was not in the right frame of mind. My poor husband, trying to juggle all the different things he had to while I was hospitalized, forgot to tell me that he put the sock bag with the rings in it into our safe. He ran home immediately to try to get me to a calmer place. COMMUNICATION! Something so necessary, yet so easily forgotten, especially when things go haywire in your life.

TRAVEL GUIDE TIPS

• *Learn about the side effects of the medication you are taking, and the remedies to alleviate the side effects.*

• *Find ways that can help you go to your "happy place." Try journal writing, art (drawing, photography), listen to music, a cleansing experience (a bubble-bath, organize drawers or closets), take a nap.*

• *Don't bite off more than you can chew. Give yourself a time limit and set boundaries.*

• *Read what you can handle. It is difficult to stay focused when on steroids and other medications. Look at magazines, newspapers or cookbooks, or listen to books on tape.*

• *Exercise - in moderation. Understand and learn about how much your body can tolerate. Practice Yoga and learn breathing exercises, especially when trying to gain back your ability to breathe.*

• *Use technology for entertainment purposes only! Stay away from researching your disease on the internet - it's easy to get hooked. Instead ask someone you trust to gather information on your situation, or call or email your doctor.*

• *Remember to go outside and look at nature. Go places that are relaxing, like the beach, or a park.*

• *Stay away from crowded places, like the mall, as your immune system is compromised.*

• *If you need to do "retail therapy" (yes, that can be quite healing), find outside shops or village centers. WARNING - if you are on steroids, you have very little restraint - leave your credit cards at home!*

CHAPTER 6

OPTIONS

"Courage is going from failure to failure without losing enthusiasm"

William Churchill

The weeks that followed my hospitalization for having pneumonia were extremely bleak for me. I didn't realize how very difficult it is to breathe and walk at the same time. I had truly believed I could just pop right back up again, and go on with life as I had always done before.

WRONG!! I had never experienced such lows as I was experiencing that dreary January. Aside from having the "post-wedding blues" and missing all the excitement this life cycle event brought to us, my daughter returned to her home in Vermont, and my body and brain were not intact. I had hit rock bottom psychologically and physically.

I was totally unaware of the havoc the drugs I had taken, and was continuing to take, were doing to my system. I had received an enormous amount of Prednisone, Bactrim, and FND – Fludarabine, Novantrone, Dexamethasone – a steroid. I had never antici-pated that I would have so many issues regarding managing the side effects of these drugs. I was dem-onstrating psychotic behaviors.

I will never forget one of the most horrible expe-riences I had as a result of being on steroids. I re-member Fred leaving for work, and I started to feel fearful, I didn't want to be left alone. Can you imagine, me, a 52 year old woman, independent for years, act-ing so unlike myself? I actually used to look forward to having "alone and quiet moments," especially after raising three children.

Embarrassed by my behavior, I would never have thought of asking my husband to stay with me a while longer. Fred always stated if I needed him, he would come right home (he luckily works 1.6 miles from our house). However, I was just to proud then to ask for help. I didn't want to appear weak. Yet as the day went by, my anxiety was getting greater, and the walls of my house started to cave in on me; it was as if I was being squeezed by the cement walls. I was horrified.

I remember running out of my house, panicked, wearing my "black chemo-jacket," white sweats and sneakers. I tried taking a power walk around my block to calm myself, I must have walked that block over 40 times. Nothing was working. I finally gave in and called Fred late in the day, screaming "I have to get out NOW!" I must have frightened him. Yet somehow, he magically understood and knew what to do.

My husband was home within 5 minutes. He bundled me up in a blanket, and put me in his car. He spoke calmly to me that I would go with him to run an errand to Staples. I started to calm down simply by hearing his voice.

When I exited the car, and entered Staples, I suddenly felt out of place, like I didn't belong there. I also felt I had the look of a "crazy person," feeling my eyes were bulging out of my head. As Fred shopped, I remember moving myself towards a wall, as if I needed support to stand. I felt so disconnected with the world. Nothing was making any sense to me. I even started to cry when I noticed the basket I was standing next to. It was a basket filled with markers, the ones I used in school. In a few short months, simply because of "the lump" I found, my life had totally changed and nothing was ever going to be the same again.

Recovering from this bout of pneumonia took about six weeks. During that time I had a reprieve from going to chemotherapy. Then I started back up again. Prior to resuming, I had been given a PET/CAT scan to measure if my lymph nodes, or as my husband so lovingly called them, "the black dots" or "cooties" had begun to disappear. Fortunately it appeared that I was having positive results...yes, we did celebrate this good news...only too prematurely.

After two more rounds of FND, I had another PET/CAT scan. I remember watching the technician's face when he was reviewing the scans, he wasn't smiling like he was the last time. I started to get anxious, and became quite demanding for I wanted him to tell me the results. He knew that doing so was totally unprofessional for he was not my doctor, but that didn't matter. I came to my own conclusion: I was in trouble.

Waiting for test results is one of the most torturous things that anyone can go through; each minute seems like an hour. You can't breathe, you remain frozen by the phone. In a weird way, it reminded me of when I was dating as a young girl, waiting for the boy who took my phone number to call me for a date. But the only date I had was with fate, and it didn't feel positive at the moment.

I always say trust yourself and your instincts. I did, and knew that when the phone rang, it was not going to be good news. It wasn't. My Non-Hodgkin Lymphoma Large B Cells were not responding to the chemotherapy I was receiving, FND. I had been advised to receive a different chemotherapy, CHOP (Cytoxan, Adriamycin or Hydroxydaunomycin, Vincristine or Oncovin, and Prednisone), but, adamant regarding not losing my hair for my daughter's wedding, I had researched an alternative "cocktail" and learned FND offered better odds for keeping your hair.

The hospital that used this protocol had had favorable results putting lymphoma into remission with FND, but the only thing I really cared about was that the statistics for losing your hair were 50/50. Indeed, my hair had thinned quite a bit and I now sported a short hair-do, but I wasn't bald. Yes, I was the sole person responsible for selecting FND.

Learning about my "failure" of the chemical agents I was using, I knew I had to go back to the drawing table. The PET/CAT scan also showed a worrisome tumor/growth in my abdomen. The oncologist I was using suggested that I should have a needle aspiration in my stomach. The thought alone made me want to run and hide.

After my freak out moment I had as a result of hearing the news that I did expect, yet hearing it made it all to real, I reached out to my sister. Betty, whom I lovingly call "Hawk-eyes," had never stopped checking me, feeling my lumps, or making sure I was OK, knew it was time again to "Stop, Look, Check and Review" my next plan of action.

It seems that when you have an illness, in my case cancer, everyone under the sun knows the best doctors. It reminded me of how when we were parents, we all knew who the best teachers were. The reality of this sentiment is totally false. You are the only one who can select whom you want to work with you, especially in the area of finding a physician you trust. Yet, being that I was not in that state of mind, I trusted other people's opinions based on hearsay, they heard what other people had to say, I listened.

When I first was diagnosed I went to a big research hospital quite far from my home. The doctor that was recommended to me was supposed to be the "best." When I met him, having been told he was top in his field, I wished I could agree. The only thing I remember is that he spoke another language. I could have used a medical interpreter.

He was telling me about specific letters and numbers, such as CD20, CD 13, that represented the cells that had created the havoc I was in right now. I was truly "lost in translation" and was mesmerized by how he didn't skip a beat when sharing with me the problem I had.

At the beginning of my cancer journey, knowing so little, this doctor had sounded so impressive. I also liked him because he supported my decision of not selecting the recommended chemotherapy cocktail, CHOP. He felt the chemotherapy I had selected, FND, had a chance of eradicating my cancer. Little did he know that the reason I had selected this medical intervention was purely based on the fact that I might not lose all of my hair.

Knowing that I was at a cross road and needed further insight, a second opinion, as to what path to take, I decided to return to him. I figured that he was well versed in lymphomas, and was familiar with my medical history. I also was sick and tired of filling out more doctor information forms. Since he had all my medical records, I knew I wouldn't have to fill out another medical form.

This time, when I entered his office, I was a more experienced "cancer traveler," already having knowledge of my disease and having had chemotherapy. I also had more knowledge regarding my illness and therefore I could ask more intelligent and meaningful questions that would shed light as to what my next step would be.

The number one question I had for him was, was it necessary to have a needle biopsy in the region of my abdomen, as the other oncologist had suggested? The other oncologist was suspicious that I had an active cancerous tumor in my abdomen, and felt the only way to diagnose this growth was do a needle biopsy.

I wanted to know whether it could be possible that what the doctor was seeing was scar tissue. I was told that the tumor in my abdomen had shrunk some due to having chemotherapy.

His response was you could never be sure, unless you have an invasive diagnostic procedure. He supported my other oncologist's need for having a needle biopsy and agreed that I should have this medical test.

I then asked him what chemotherapy I should have next as my lymphoma was no longer responding to FND. The way he responded to me reminded me of a wonderful New York comedian, Jackie Mason. Jackie, using his delightful NY and Yiddish accent, always responded to questions asked of him in the following manner, "You could do it this way, yet, on the other hand, you could do it that way," always leaving the person who asked the question totally confused as to what he was really saying.

This doctor did the exact same thing, "You could have this chemotherapy, or better yet, you could select that therapy." Then, leaving me totally bewildered, he stated, "Better yet, do nothing. You are just fine, let's watch and wait, see what happens in 6 months, go have a good time, enjoy yourself, and play tennis."

My initial response to his suggestion of doing nothing was delight! But instinctively I knew that I had to be "The Master Of My Own Fate, become The Captain Of My Own Soul" – William Ernest Henley. I thanked the doctor, turned around with Fred, and did what any person would do in my situation, knowing the best deli in LA was across the street.

We went to the deli and had a huge pastrami sandwich, french fries, and a piece of seven layer cake. For a slight moment, I forgot about my illness, which was an almost impossibility.

Wherever I went, my lymphoma went with me, "Me and My Cancerous Shadow." Even when looking in the mirror, I could no longer just see me, the body that I had lived in for 52 years. I saw terrified eyes, a third breast (my porto-catheter) and thinning hair.

TRAVEL GUIDE TIPS

• *REMEMBER – no matter how much everyone loves you, wants the best for you, it is your body, your decision, only you know what it is like to face this enormous challenge. Do your homework – think about what kind of doctor suits you best, listen to others with half an ear, and trust yourself.*

• *Do not minimize your physical situation or problem. Time is of the essence, be honest, ask for help.*

• *Know where there is a 24 hour pharmacy and be prepared for emergencies. Always have back up when you are alone, and your mate is not reachable via cell phone.*

• *Try to stay calm during an emergency situation, you can make your physical symptoms worse when you are panicked. Remember to "Breathe", and learn visualization techniques, learn how to take yourself out of what is happening around you, and go to that special place. It does take practice and concentration, yet eventually, you will know how to quickly transition yourself.*

• *Make plans for days you do not have to be at the doctor. Go out to eat, treat yourself well, yet be cautious regarding your compromised immune system; especially being around children. Explain to your younger family members that you have to be careful because germs, even though invisible, can make you sick. Make sure all kids understand the importance of washing their hands.*

CHAPTER 7

DREAMS VERSUS REALITY

"Success is thinking big, aiming high, and shooting far. It's taking a dream and doing anything, risking everything , and stopping at nothing to make it a reality."

Caroline Kent

Throughout the year of "The Chemotherapy Challenges" to see if I could have a positive response to the medical agents used on me, I had only one goal in my mind, one focus, and one dream that I wanted more than anything: to be back to where I belonged, back in my classroom, teaching.

Officially, as a teacher who had a medical leave of absence, I had to share with the school district I worked in by March what my plans were for the following school year. There was no question in my mind that I would be returning to my profession, my passion. I told the Head of Personnel Services I would be returning officially in September.

The general public who are not teachers don't realize the amount of planning that goes into opening up a classroom; how you want your room set up, where the important interactive boards should be placed in your room (i.e. Word Wall), organizing your library, setting up your centers, setting up your seats in order to help facilitate learning for all students, etc. I was in the zone once I told the district, my principal, and my partner (I shared a contract with a most amazing teacher, who stood by my side with her most generous support during my absence) that I would be teaching again.

I was so sure that I was doing what I had to do to get well, I would be healthy again, the medicines would work and September was just around the corner. I even started thinking of which welcoming poem I would put in front of my classroom door. It went like this:

September Days are glad days,

for school has now begun,

We'll have to work and study hard,

But also we'll have fun!

Maude Grant

The Instructor, 1926

In April, 2004 I was asked to attend a Child Study Meeting regarding a young man who was going to be placed in my class. Being that I was a full inclusion teacher (having a class population that includes special needs children i.e. Autism, Down's Syndrome), I was to attend this meeting in order to get to know more about the student's needs for the following academic year.

I can't begin to describe the feelings I had that day. I was on a high. I was back where I belonged. I was listening to "teacher talk" instead of "chemo talk." No one in the room had IV lines, including myself. The teachers had outfits that were so colorful. I was part of a team, collaborating to help make a difference in the life of a student, and working in partnership with the student's parents who had enumerable challenges.

My brain cells felt alive. I was being creative. I was not patient #24765, but Mrs. Pardes, an elementary teacher at Trabuco Mesa Elementary School in Rancho Santa Margarita.

After leaving the meeting, I remember walking on the campus, just marveling at the beauty of the school and the mountains surrounding the buildings. I saw many of my students, and hugged every single one of them. Sheer Joy!! One of the students proudly said that she had her hair cut off just for me and donated it to "Locks of Love." What a majestic day that was for me!!

Red Tape! In every administration, one must have to go through red tape in order to get all your paper work up to date. In my case, due to the fact that I was on a medical leave for cancer, I had to go to an oncologist selected by the school district, to verify that I was physically able to return to teacher duty. They also had to have him review if there were any necessary accommodations that needed to be implemented for me in order to keep me physiologically safe.

The school district contacted me at the end of May, I was to make an appointment ASAP, then in June, a meeting would be held with the head of personal services, my principal, my partner and myself (and if I needed assistance to get there that person could also attend).

I immediately made the appointment with the school appointed oncologist (the school wanted no conflict of interest which is certainly understandable). I expected to just go in, talk for two minutes, and have him sign off on the application stating that I was in good health and ready to report for duty.

I WAS DETERMINED TO SUCCEED...TO GO BACK TO WHERE I WAS NEEDED, TO IMPACT THE LIVES OF MY STUDENTS, TO BROADEN THEIR HORIZONS, TO SEE MIRACLES HAPPEN, TO HELP THEIR DREAMS BECOME THEIR REALITIES, MAKE A DIFFERENCE IN THE LIFE OF A CHILD TODAY, THEREFORE TOUCHING THEIR TOMORROWS.

ABRAHAM LINCOLN STATED, "YOUR OWN RESOLUTION TO SUCCEED IS MORE IMPORTANT THAN ANY OTHER ONE THING."

The day I entered the school appointed oncologist's office, I had a good feeling. First I was greeted by the most delicious smell of coffee. This doctor truly understood how to make patients feel welcome and soothed. Then the receptionist, a male, whose manner was so kind and inviting, welcomed me, handed me "WITH EXPLANATION" on how to fill out the necessary medical forms (I think he truly understood how when one goes through this lengthy journey which includes multiple visits to so many new doctors, the last thing you want to do is fill out another form). He told me the doctor would see me shortly. My anxiety level was lowered simply by being surrounded by this type of environment.

After waiting about 20 minutes, which is certainly not long according to "the world of the waiting room," a very jolly, smiling oncologist greeted me. I explained my situation and why I was there, and handed him a file that I personally had made highlighting my diagnosis, chemotherapy interventions, and other pertinent information.

I was well trained as a patient that most visits with physicians last a short period of time. I did have some oncologists/physicians who were generous with their time, yet with them sometimes seeing as many as 40 patients daily, it is impossible to have long visits. I fondly called certain doctors the "In and Out" doctors. I never understood how they could listen to the patient, get accurate information, give an appropriate diagnosis, and educate the patient in that short period of time.

What happened next was not expected. The school appointed oncologist actually took time out to review my file "slowly."

After reading all of my information, he looked at me and asked me to sit next to him at his computer. He proceeded to explain to me everything there is to know about the type of cancer I had: B Cell Lymphoplasma-cytic Lymphoma, demonstrating what my mutated cells looked like on the computer screen. This particular lymphoma, a malignancy of the white blood cells and plasma, can be best evaluated by removing the en-larged lymph node, performing a cellular microscopic morphology, marker molecule expression, and looking for specific tumor associated gene defects.

This oncologist also informed me that doing a needle biopsy was not the appropriate diagnostic choice when you had the type of blood cancer that I had. You don't have a good chance of probing a larger than normal node, or retrieving a cancerous lymphocytic cell (my sister also felt this way from the onset of my "lump," and was strongly suspicious that my results from the needle biopsy were not definitive. She believed that I needed to have the node removed and sent to a pathologist. Betty knew that my elevated titer and eosinophil levels were indicative of lymphoma, not mono).

Looking at the blood levels that were written on my submitted medical charts, and other medical results, the school appointed oncologist explained that the chemotherapy that I had received to date was just a short, stop-measure which would halt the disease for a little while. My symptoms, which included horrible night sweats, major leg and abdominal cramps, loss of appetite, loss of weight, and feeling extremely fatigued, would return when my disease revisited me.

After spending almost two hours with me, the oncologist said my lymphoma would never go away, and it could get worse. My only chance, the one treatment that might possibly cure me, was a bone marrow transplant. I needed to have a Bone Marrow Transplant ASAP.

TRAVEL GUIDE TIPS

• *Always be prepared for the unexpected; you may "will" your outcome according to your wishes, yet think about what is best for you in the long run.*

• *Learn what is to be expected from your treatment. What are your goals and objectives? How long can the medical intervention (chemotherapy) keep the cancerous cells at bay? What are the benefits to different forms of chemotherapy or other interventions?*

• *Try to understand a very difficult concept, you can never go home again. Once you are removed from something that is familiar to you for a long period of time, nothing is ever the same.*

• *People who greet you after you have been absent for a long period of time due to illness feel awkward. They don't know how to speak to you, and might make inappropriate comments that might be offensive to you i.e. "You look so good." (I hated that comment, how did I look to everyone before I had cancer?) Try to understand how difficult it is for them to address you. Be aware of their discomfort. Try to make conversation to put them at ease. When asked how are your feeling, try to find an upbeat response that has a positive intonation. For example, "my journey was challenging, but I learned so much. Or you can happily respond with something that you both share that validates your "aliveness," like "I am still breathing." Or "I am happily alive." No one knows what tomorrow can bring. The bottom line is Enjoy your Now! Every breath you take is precious.*

CHAPTER 8

BE PREPARED TO LOSE AND LEARN

"You're going to lose more than you're going to win, no matter who you are. Most of us overreact when we lose, and over-celebrate when we win, and I'm no exception. I have a love-hate relationship with losing: it makes me brooding and quarrelsome. But the fact is, a loss is its own inevitable lesson, and it can be just as valuable as a victory in the range of experiences, if you'll examine it."

Lance Armstrong

When you listen to an oncologist at the beginning of your illness, you are in shock with no understanding of what is really going on, nothing makes any sense. You can not think clearly, you have no focus of your present reality.

You are overwhelmed by people sharing their opinions of what you should do to find the cure for your cancer. At first, their sharing information appears very helpful. But your feelings change once you have been in the trenches, receiving chemotherapy, and having many other medical procedures done to you.

You become a little bit tougher, more empowered. Though anxiety exists, you adjust to your new medical environment, learning to understand some of the lingo that the medical professionals use in regards to your treatment and prognosis.

You even fall into a routine when you go to Chemoland. My husband, Fred, would bring me to the lab, making sure I was settled in. I would be greeted warmly by the medical team, we'd have our favorite discussions, one of which was on who were we voting for on American Idol. Fred would wait for my porto-catheter to be accessed, which was difficult as the device was deeply planted in my chest (I had requested that I should have as little bulge as possible showing for I didn't want anyone to see what I called my "third breast"). He would sit patiently, rubbing my feet, waiting for me to fall asleep, which was a happy side effect of the drugs I was receiving. My mother would pick me up afterwards, and we would discuss what restaurant we should eat in.

Having chemotherapy, and even hearing that you have to go for multiple rounds of chemo, is one thing. However, when you hear that all chemotherapy you've been given to eradicate your cancer has not been successful, and that, nothing except a BONE MARROW TRANSPLANT might work, you can never be prepared to deal with that type of failure. I had truly believed that the chemo drugs I was being given would work and I would be cured.

Psychologically, the mere mention of the words Bone Marrow Transplant, triggered enormous emotions of fear, panic and anxiety. I had no concept of what was involved in this type of procedure. I also had no understanding how your life, as well as those you live with, would be impacted. But I knew I didn't want one.

The school appointed oncologist was quite intuitive and sensitive, and while I turned a lovely shade of gray, he reassured me of the success rate of bone marrow transplants. He further explained how that choice is the right choice for my form of aggressive lymphoma. He stated that there are present discussions at lymphoma conferences that patients with this type of cancer should skip chemotherapy altogether, as patients have a better chance of curing their lymphoma by going directly to having a transplant. They avoid the multiple and long term side effects of chemo, which at times can trigger a secondary cancer.

I listened with almost "two ears," yet I still had my own agenda. I wasn't ready to let go of the possibility that I was going to teach in September. The oncologist, who was most generous with his time, considering I wasn't even his patient, bid me good-bye and good luck. He told me he was going to mail his report to the head of personnel at my district. They, in turn, would contact me, and set up a meeting to discuss his findings, and plans for my return back to teach.

There is no question that I was in denial regarding the severity of my condition. The words the oncologist shared with me went in one ear and out the other. All I knew was that I was going to go to a school meeting regarding my medical release and to see if the school district needed to make any accommodations for me upon my return.

The meeting was scheduled for the end of May. I couldn't wait to sign the contract as a re-hire for the next academic year. I even contacted my partner saying "it is time to get ready and plan for our future students."

I was so happy. I was going to be "normal" again, wake up in the morning, rush through breakfast, barely reading the paper, quickly go to the bathroom, shower, and put on my teacher clothes (yes, I am one of those teachers that dresses thematically according to the holidays), drive to work, thinking of the plans for the day.

No more seeing doctors, no more waiting rooms, no more feeling like I have been put out to pasture, I'd be back in the world I missed so much! I couldn't wait.

Was my thinking realistic? Absolutely not! It is very easy to convince yourself, and construct what you desire to happen, not entertaining a thought of the possibility it might not go the way you expect.

The days went quickly. Before I knew it, May was here and I was going to the meeting. I couldn't wait for it to happen.

The following week, on a Wednesday, at 11:00 a.m., one of my dear close friends who also happens to be a teacher, drove me to the district office. I remember not really feeling especially anxious in the car, for I felt all would go smoothly. This was just a formality. All the paper work would be reviewed, the contract would be signed, and I would be teaching in September.

As I entered the district office, I was greeted by my partner, who was so joyful we would be teaching together! We had been sitting in the waiting area for about ten minutes, when in came my principal, looking so grand and professional in her light pink St. John's outfit. She smiled at me, and stated that she had been asked to go back first to see the Director of Personnel Services, and then they would call us in. Even at that point, I had no clue about my impending detour and that things were not going to go the way I expected. I just thought that the professionals in charge had to review the pertinent paper work for my re-entry.

Time moved forward, but we remained in the front office, waiting for our names to be called so we could enter into the director's office.

WAITING!! No matter how you think you have patience, and that you can just sit back, relax, and read a magazine until you are called, it is absolutely not true. You begin to play "Watch The Clock" games, checking every second to see if the hour or minute hands moved. It is magic how when you play this game, those hands never seem to move, or if they do, it is at a snail's pace. Then the body takes over, knowing that something doesn't feel right, something is very wrong. Your heart begins to pound, your sweat glands go into overdrive, you feel you need to camp out in the bathroom and do your business – continually, and your mouth is totally dry.

After a very long 20 minute wait, we entered the meeting room. I looked at my principal, the smile she originally had on her face was no longer there. I looked at the director of personnel, who is always so personable with me, and she, too, looked more on the rigid side, giving me a terse smile. As I sat down, I thought for a second that my nerves were getting in the way, and that I was just imagining things.

I forgot my own rule, and didn't follow my own advice... "trust yourself, trust your instincts, if you feel something is unusual, it usually is true."

The director started the meeting by stating how happy she was to see me, how the school population missed me, and my future students were going to be so happy to have me in the classroom again.

She then proceeded to have us look at my file, a copy had been placed in front of each of us. The cover letter of the file stated what the purpose of the meeting was; to re-instate Michelle Pardes as an Elementary School Teacher at Trabuco Mesa. The director then asked us to turn to the next page, where there was a list of accommodations that we had to review, based on the oncologist's findings, to be implemented upon my return. She proceeded to read the accommodations, such as limiting my yard duty, putting in an air filter in the classroom so the germs could be taken out, leaving me with better quality air to prevent me from getting sick (my immune system was compromised due to all the chemotherapy I'd had). While she was going over the list, it appeared that all was in order. I was sure the following page would just be the signature page, I would sign, then go on my way.

The director, prior to us having turn to the third, and last page of the report, stopped, looked around the room, resting her eyes on me. She proceeded to say that many things don't go your way, no matter how badly you might want it or will it to happen. She also said that the school district was looking out for my well being, and the oncologist that I was sent to was my advocate. His job was to make sure I was capable physically of being back at work.

A feeling of uneasiness enveloped me. I sensed that I needed to use my inferential skills to interpret what she was really saying. I found out right after she stopped introducing the third page. As she told us to turn to the third page, she reminded us again that the decision was made in the best interest of both the teacher and the students the teacher was going to teach.

On the bottom of the page, there were two boxes. One box stated that the doctor's findings confirmed that the teacher could be re-instated for the upcoming academic year. The second box stated that based on the doctor's findings, the teacher was incapable of going back to teach.

Looking at the boxes, I saw the second box checked off. Tears began to swell in my eyes. I looked up at everyone sitting with me, and they too, had tears. They genuinely empathized as to how badly I wanted to return, yet it was not going to happen. Not yet.

The first time I cried uncontrollably was when I was first told I had lymphoma, in the oncologist's office, the previous October. Here we were in May, 2004. My sobbing was filled with pain, disappointment, heartache that my desire to return to teach was not going to happen. I couldn't stop crying.

They say that crying is contagious. When you hear someone cry, the painful sound that it makes can stimulate your own tear ducts, and tears begin to flow.

That is exactly what happened at the meeting. All those that were sitting around the table began to cry. Five amazing, warm and wonderful friends and professionals, who were there to cheer for me as my dream of returning to school was realized, felt my pain and disappointment. There are times when words are not to be used, one just has to feel it and go through the process of loss. Human touch can help. A warm embrace, a loving pat on your back, or taking some-one's hand and holding it can be comforting.

We exited the meeting with hugs, and reassur-ances that the day would come when I would be healthy again, and would return to teach. I remember feeling totally numb after the meeting, feeling that I was facing another brick wall, another obstacle. At that point, I couldn't even think of how I was going to climb the wall, let alone get to the other side, where the cancer journey would be behind me.

TRAVEL GUIDE TIPS

• *Learn about the power of educating yourself with the variety of options you have. The treatment that might appear most frightening to you, may be the choice that will bring you the strongest possibility of a cure.*

• *Use the time when you are home to try to broaden your horizons. We are all creatures of comfort and, at times, resist change. Try to envision yourself exploring other avenues that you might learn to enjoy.*

• *Try to "dig deep" and realize your own amazing strength and fortitude. Embrace scary options, go towards it with an understanding that you need to take huge risks to accomplish your most important goal, your return to good health.*

• *Read inspirational, motivational and spiritual material. Get in touch with yourself by learning of others who survived unbelievable challenges in life.*

• *Visit with your Rabbi or Pastor. They can help provide you with what is necessary to help get you through your journey spiritually, with faith and understanding..*

CHAPTER 9

FINDING SUPPORT

"No one in this life gets ahead without the help of a lot of other people. Even the most talented need others to point out the way or lend a hand."

Tavis Smiley

After the school meeting, a very close friend, who has been by my side from the beginning of my cancer journey, drove me to meet her sister-in-law, my sister Betty, and my mother for dinner. My sister and her sister-in-law are both Nurse Practitioners, therefore quite knowledgeable about the medical world.

We were meeting at one of my favorite fish restaurants down at the harbor in Dana Point. I didn't feel like eating or seeing anyone, especially my family. My hair was disheveled, and my shirt was drenched from my tears. I was devastated. I also knew they had been through so much with me. I didn't want to put them through any more of my emotional roller coaster ride.

Needless to say, you can act totally different in front of a stranger, but when it comes to people who know you well, they can just look at you and know something is very wrong.

After sitting down and having the medicine I needed immediately, a Lemon Drop Martini, I proceeded to tell them what happened at the school meeting. I also stated that the oncologist was convinced that the only thing that could save me was having a bone marrow transplant.

Saying the words BONE MARROW TRANSPLANT out loud, again started my tears flowing. I got quite hysterical, declaring that I was NOT going ahead and having one. Betty, who was the most familiar with my case, and had been doing research for months on finding the right treatment for me, wanted me to go for a consultation with an extraordinary hematologist, Dr. Alexander Levine, at USC, Norris Cancer Institute, the same hematologist my father saw when he was ill with leukemia. She felt that after having a consultation with this most knowledgeable and experienced doctor on lymphoma, the information I would receive would further validate that my only option for "Cure and Survival" was getting a bone marrow transplant.

Betty looked at me, with that serious, no fooling around stare, and said bluntly, "you have to do what it takes no matter what is involved, even if it means having a bone marrow transplant, for THE FAMILY!!!"

After hearing her loud and clear, I knew deep in my heart, that no matter what, I would do what it took to live.

What goes down, must come back up again...I couldn't waste any more time.

After my melt down, I put my "action hat" back on and started the process of getting hold of my "life line." I needed to arrange a consultation with Dr. Levine, the hematologist at USC, Norris. Easier said than done... she was not taking many new patients due to administrative duties and research.

Two heads are better than one, my mom had a plan how to get past the secretary at USC and get in direct contact with the doctor I needed to see.

Name dropping can work. My mother spoke to the secretary and let her know that she was the wife of Julius Glantz, a former patient of Dr. Levine. The doctor at USC had worked so diligently to save my father's life; including getting him into a clinical study at Scripps Hospital, in La Jolla. She was amazed at how he survived the horrors of being in a concentration camp. She had admired his character, strength and determination to do anything to survive.

Emotional and familial connections do work! The doctor called my mother back within a few hours. Per Dr. Levine's request, I had to overnight all my original slides taken from my neck biopsy...all 152 slides...plus all of my medical reports and scan results.

To make matters more challenging, I had 24 hours to get them to her for time was of the essence. She wanted to do her own pathology investigation prior to my arranged appointment which was going to be in two weeks.

Nothing is impossible when your life is on the line. My mother and I ran to Hoag Hospital, gathered all the necessary slides and reports, ran to a shipping store, packed it all up, and shipped it Overnight.

The contents were going to have to get to USC without getting lost (I couldn't get replacements of those slides for they were the originals). I said a special prayer over that box. It contained my chances of potential options for eradicating this cancer that wouldn't leave me alone.

Lost, confused, terrified, and frozen. I didn't know how I was going to get through the next two weeks until I was going to see this amazing doctor

Thankfully, I had my my support group. It was a genuine blessing to have people who understood my journey in my life at the time I needed support most.

I will never forget at the very beginning of my illness, my reluctance to join a cancer support group. At first I felt like I didn't belong to that population for I didn't really accept my diagnosis. I didn't understand the fact that lymphoma and cancer had become part of my life, never really leaving me.

After much thought, feeling so alone, I decided to investigate a highly recommended support group, The Wellness Center. I called to make an appointment. From the minute I spoke to the person on the other end of the telephone, I felt a sense of relief that someone out there understood how I felt. I went for an interview, and officially signed on to join a weekly cancer support group close to where I lived.

Feeling connected and understood validates the statement I had read that when one is going through the journey of cancer and chemotherapy, there is a higher success rate of the possibility of reaching a "healing place" by having knowledgeable guides lead the way. As Kate Bush stated, "All we're ever looking for is another open door". I certainly felt fortunate to have found that entrance for in addition to my ongoing illness, I was still suffering from depression that my daughter's wedding was over, and that she was no longer living next to her family.

Equally difficult was dealing with my bout of pneumonia, I was still having difficulties in breathing and walking. I was also suffering major side effects from all the Prednisone I was taking. I was extremely lonely and felt totally cut off from the world.

Fred, trying his best to cheer me up, called me every hour, checking in to make sure I was okay.

Somehow I resented this type of phone call for I knew he didn't have enough time in the day to really hear my response to his questions, "How are you? Are you Okay?" I only wanted to engage in lengthy conversations regarding all the feelings I was going through. But I felt I had to say I was doing okay for I didn't want to worry him or become a burden.

After a few weeks of these perfunctory phone calls, I blew up at my husband. I was feeling sorry for myself, and jealous that he got to leave the house and go to work. I was tired of giving him the response that made him comfortable. It felt like everyone I met expected that response - no one wants to deal with the many trying moments a person with cancer goes through.

I told Fred to stop calling. I was tired of always having to say "I am okay" when I didn't feel like it. If he felt like calling, he should come up with a better question, one that I could relate to.

He did. Five minutes later, he called and asked, "Still Breathing?" I burst out into laughter. Those two words symbolized that yes, I should be grateful, for I was very much alive, just like my husband. We all have challenges, and as long as you are still breathing you can make choices as to how to live your life, no matter how difficult. That was a turning point for me. I knew how to make lemonade out of lemons, and I chose to continue to make that drink throughout my cancer and survivorship.

Luckily, the day after I sent my slides to USC, was my meeting with my support group. The leader of the group, Dr. Sandra Weiss, a psychologist and most wise and compassionate woman, understood the art of listening and promoting the group to engage in meaningful conversations and interactions. As I entered the meeting room, the leader immediately picked up through my atypical greeting and body language that I was carrying a heavy load. Through her perception, she geared the group towards an issue I was obviously troubled with.

Reflecting back to that moment, I was truly one who was extremely blessed in that group. I had an option, a choice with the possibility of eradicating my cancer. Others in the group had so many difficult cancers and side effects, both physiological and emotional that they were dealing with. One, an amazing man, was a physician who captured the true essence of tenacity and determination. He'd had cancer revisit him six times, each visit required life altering surgeries, the last one is when he had his vocal chords removed. He taught all of us the meaning of being flexible and adapting to your new body; mastering a talking device that allowed us to hear him speak.

Another person, who also was an amazing hero (he is with us in spirit), battled pancreatic cancer for over nine years. He taught us that no mountain was too high to climb in order to stay alive. He had over 200 types of chemotherapy, traveling all over the

world in search of the right cure, visiting with sha-
mans and others who practiced with different medicines and thought outside the box.

His courage and quest for living will never be
forgotten. He also had the ability to help others focus
on dealing with the difficult issues we all faced, including my going for a bone marrow transplant. According to him, as long as you have a choice to live there
really is no decision to make. Living is always your
number one choice.

One of the issues that was always discussed was
worrying whether you are going to live or die. A very
bright older gentleman who was a chemist, always
smiled when we had this discussion.

He put things in the right perspective. He responded to the issue of "worrying" by responding,
"Worry, why worry, no matter how much you worry,
the inevitable will happen anyway. No amount of
worrying will stop anything from happening. Besides,
why worry, my wife worries enough for the both of
us." His outlook in life spiritually remains inside me.

The members in our group always remained positive, and supportive. New members joined, with major challenges creating havoc in their lives. Collabora-
tively, with our "Weiss" leadership, we helped those
that suffered navigate the challenges of their diagnosis
and helped them find effective ways to cope.

We also helped find meaningful avenues to travel on with our family members, the caretakers, for they had their own issues to deal with.

Having this supportive strength behind me, along with a loving family who wanted me to stay alive at any cost, empowered me to go forward and open a new door that had HOPE written on it.

TRAVEL GUIDE TIPS

• *Recognize that during this trying time you have a need to be surrounded by those that can help you navigate your diagnosis, and support you every step of the way. Get involved with a support group that addresses your needs. Find one that can also provide support to your caregivers. They also need a shoulder to lean on. They have their own set of challenges; this journey is new for them too.*

• *Know that support is necessary when you are hospitalized. Find out or have your caretaker find out what provisions you have regarding your medical and psychological challenges.*

• *Recognizing that support groups may be uncomfortable for some, get help from a licensed therapist who is familiar with the world you are in now. Establish a relationship with someone you feel connected with for the journey of cancer is ongoing; there are many diverse challenges ahead for you and those that are involved with your care.*

• *Try to understand that there is no "short cut" when it comes to finding a CURE. There are trials and errors, things don't always go the way you expect them to go. Remember, you are STILL BREATHING, try to equip yourself with as much hope and patience as you can.*

CHAPTER 10

EXITING PLANET EARTH

"You gain strength, courage, and confidence by every experience in which you really stop to look fear in the face."

Eleanor Roosevelt

FEAR – an unpleasant feeling of anxiety or apprehension caused by the presence or anticipation of danger.

WORRY – a concern about something that threatens to bring bad news or results.

My entry into the "World of Chemotherapy" started in November, 2003. Eight months later, I had had multiple drugs dripped into my veins, experienced pneumonia, Thrush (infection in the mouth), infected toes, inability to taste food, shortness of breath, extreme fatigue, neuropathy (constant tingling in your hands and toes), and I STILL NEEDED TO GET TO MY FINISH LINE...BEING CURED.

To continue what Eleanor Roosevelt said, "I lived through this horror, I can take the next thing that comes along.

The danger lies in refusing to face the fear, in not daring to come to grips with it. If you fail anywhere along the line it will take away your confidence. You must make yourself succeed every time. YOU MUST DO THE THING YOU THINK YOU CANNOT DO."

Once more, with overwhelming feelings of sheer terror and fright, I reflected back to the important lessons I taught my students.

On the first day of school, after our introductions and tour of the school, rules were introduced into the classroom. The one guideline that I felt was so important for the children to learn, follow and integrate, was to always try their very best, to think, even risking failure, that they could do anything they put their minds to.

After introducing this concept by reading "The Little Engine That Could," I had hidden behind my chair a white piece of paper with the following words written on it, "I CAN'T." I proceeded to let them know that those two words were not allowed in my classroom. We were going to tear those words up (using volunteers in the classroom we tore that sign into small pieces) and throw them out of our minds, and place those scraps of paper into the trash can.

I then held up a sign, much larger with bold print stating, "I think I can – I think I can – I think I can – I think I can."

The students, after reflecting on their own personal successes when they'd first thought they couldn't succeed (first and second graders have such great goals, to be able to ride a two wheeler without falling down, to stay balanced on the Monkey Beam in the park, be able to swim, and ALL wanted to be able to read a book of their own choice), repeated a phrase that was always revisited in my class room...I THINK I CAN!

Being a teacher also means you are a student; a life student. You are also a role model. Thinking again of how important it was to reconnect with the world I loved, teaching, I decided I would do everything in my power to come back, and teach.

I also knew I wasn't ready yet to leave "Planet Earth" permanently. I had a husband who needed me. (Who was going to pick up his socks, make sure he takes his pills, remind him of his social plans which he always forgot within a minute a me telling him, names of people he can't remember, and the most important thing, to love him and share many more wonderful life experiences with him?) Leaving my other family members wasn't an option either. I wanted to see my adult children living "happily ever after," having loving mates. I wanted to experience being a grandmother; I was told that wearing "that hat" is the most wonderful feeling in the world. Some even say, "skip parenthood, go straight to grandparenthood," you get to experience all the joys, and none of the difficulties of raising children. I also knew that Betty worked so hard in making sure I would be successful. I was her "life long best friend" and her partner, working side by side with her making sure our mother was well cared for. Growing up as I had, seeing other parents' sorrow after losing and burying their children, there was no way I WASN'T GOING TO DO WHAT IT TOOK!!!

I NEEDED TO TAKE THE ROAD TO RECOVERY.

I HAD TO PACK UP ALL MY COURAGE, STRENGTH, TENACITY, FAITH...AND DECIDE TO GO

"On the road again," just like Willie Nelson.

AND THAT IS EXACTLY WHAT I DID!

On a beautiful, clear day, my mother, sister and I climbed into my mother's white Honda car to meet with Dr. Levine, at USC Norris Cancer Center. We were to have a consultation regarding her findings (she did her own pathology report on my slides), and my best options to getting "Cured."

My nervous energy was at a Level 10+, therefore sitting in the car looking out the window was not going to be possible. I needed to have something to focus on to not let my mind take me to those dark and terrifying places. I convinced my mother and sister that I needed to be the driver.

While I was on a very crowded freeway heading north towards USC Medical Center, Betty, who is always looking out for my well being, tried to prepare me for what she suspected would happen: a discussion of topics that I might not find very comforting, especially since I had already gone through so many medical interventions without success.

She attempted to broach the one subject I was the most terrified of... a bone marrow transplant. By the sheer mentioning of the possibility, I started to cry. Not a great thing to do while you are driving. My being upset also was contagious. My adorable French mother, when agitated, always reverts back to speaking French, which my sister and I both understand. She got angry that Betty was bringing up topics that might not even happen.

After a few moments of silence, while we were slowly crawling towards Los Angeles, my sister brought up the subject of talking. She knows that I love to "exercise my lips"...talk a lot. She felt that during this most important consultation I needed to do "less talking, more listening."

Miraculously, we arrived at USC three hours later, in one piece. After being challenged to find a parking spot in a lot specified for Norris Cancer Center, we proceeded to Dr. Levine's office, a place I had visited so many times with my father.

Revisiting that time in my mind reassured me that Dr. Levine was an "Angel of Hope." No matter how grave my father's medical condition was, we were always left with a feeling of hope and possible miracles.

After being shown to her office, we went into "waiting mode." Betty, once again anticipating what would be needed in order to understand our options and make the right choice for me, directed my mom to be the "scribe." She was to write down exactly what was being said by the doctor.

After 30 minutes of waiting, Dr. Levine entered the room. Her entry was certainly NOT what I expected. Her style with me was the opposite of her style with my father. Instead of being "warm and fuzzy" and doing "chit chat," she immediately stated in a very firm voice, "MICHELLE, YOU HAVE GOT A NASTY CASE OF LYMPHOMA!"

The impossible happened, I went from being a "talker" to becoming mute, and my lips remained sealed for almost three hours. I started sweating profusely. My head felt like I was burning (I was wearing a net under my blond wig). The more the Dr. Levine talked about my options, the faster the sweat poured out of my wig. I looked like I was going to melt away, paralleling the scene from "The Wizard of Oz" when The Wicked Witch of The West melts down into the floor.

My mother, who was once a professional secretary/administrative assistant and extremely talented at writing in short hand, was just doodling with her pen. Dr. Levine, in addition to being an exceptional doctor, is an exceptional teacher.

While she was speaking of all of my alternatives, Dr. Levine was writing down all that went with my options; side effects of the drugs, the molecular designs, potential of going into remission, how long would I stay in remission, would the disease return? My head was literally spinning.

Luckily, Betty, the medical expert of my case, was able to follow and understand what was being presented. Needless to say, my sister was right about Dr. Levine bringing up the fact that I needed to have an Autologous Bone Marrow Transplant (autologous meant the cells used for the transplant would be coming from my body). Any other choice presented by her was only going to be a stop gap measure for the type of lymphoma I had; Lymphoplasmacytic Lymphoma - B Cell Lineage - C20 positive B Cells, Express CD 43, and CD 23, Negative for CD 5, Stage 4 - Transitioned into the aggressive form of the disease.

Dr. Levine strongly suggested that I contact City of Hope ASAP, and arrange to meet the bone marrow team, which included an exceptional hematologist/oncologist, Dr. Popplewell. She also mentioned that City of Hope was in the midst of doing innovative research using targeted therapy with radiation (this type of therapy is done in lieu of whole body radiation, resulting in less harmful side effects. Targeted therapy would only destroy bad cells, not good cells).

I remember leaving her office in a state of shock. Dr. Levine's "dose of reality" was difficult for me to process. I didn't know how I was going to muster up the physical and emotional strength to face another battle. I just wanted to move on with my life, and never have to discuss chemotherapy or radiation again.

That sentiment was also shared by my husband. A lawyer, Fred could not attend the medical consultation with me that day for he had to make a court appearance. I had convinced him that I would be just fine, and he should just go do what he had to do.

Hearing my sister tell him on the phone that I had to have a bone marrow transplant was too much for him to bear. He had walked by my side through the last nine months, going to Chemoland with me, diligently rubbing my feet to relax me before I received my multiple colored infusions, watching me go through so many difficult side effects. He, too, couldn't believe that a bone marrow transplant was now my only viable option. The mere mention of having this procedure unnerved him. It also meant that I REALLY HAD A DIFFICULT CASE OF CANCER THAT WOULD NOT DISAPPEAR WITH THE USUAL CHEMOTHERAPY INTERVENTIONS.

After speaking to him, still in a state of shock, I wanted to have Dim Sum; something my father, mother and I always did when we went to see Dr. Levine.

What I forgot was in my mental state I could have used a more serene environment, not one where there is so much activity going on. Although I thought I could eat, I could only manage a "liquid lunch." I was feeling very little, and that further numbed me. I didn't understand how all those people in the restaurant could be happily engaged in conversation with each other, while I was facing a potential death sentence.

The mood during the car ride going home was much more subdued. I just couldn't process the information that I was not going back to teach. Instead, I had to start up again making phone calls, trying to get a doctor's appointment at City of Hope.

It is amazing that 24 hours after Dr. Levine's consultation, I went from being mentally unable to cope with what I had to do, to going into action mode, making the necessary arrangements to see the oncologist at City of Hope for a BONE MARROW TRANSPLANT.

TRAVEL GUIDE TIPS

• *Have directions to where you are going, and a back up plan in case you are stuck in traffic.*

• *Find out where the most convenient parking lot is for your your destination, and if there is a back up parking lot in case it is full.*

• *Bring your Handicap Placard in case you are using someone else's vehicle.*

• *Prior to going to a consultation, see if you are allowed to bring a tape recorder to record the information given. If not, make sure you bring a trusted person who will act as the "recorder" and scribe what transpires.*

• *Communicate with those that are accompanying you regarding your emotional state, and how much you can handle regarding discussions that can frighten you.*

• *Have a designated person communicates with your loved ones to inform them of the status of your health and types of medical interventions you are having or will have in the future. Make sure you give guidelines to the "Reporter" as to how much information you want people to know.*

• *When going to the hospital / labs for tests, learn about the different restaurants you want to eat at that are geo-graphically close to your destination. Looking forward to "your edible reward" does help your focus while you are being placed "under the scope" - or used as a pin cushion.*

CHAPTER 11

POWER FORWARD

"I am not discouraged, because every wrong attempt discarded is another step forward."

Thomas Edison

City of Hope has the perfect name. From the onset of my initial contact with them, the receptionist made me feel welcome. I was given an appointment within two days of my calling them.

Going to City of Hope with my mother and husband was a totally different experience than I had going to USC Norris Cancer Center. This time I was resolved to confront my situation, I felt I was going in a positive direction that would bring me healing and recovery. I had come to meet Dr. Popplewell, their lead oncologist, and the Bone Marrow Transplant Team.

When you arrive at City of Hope you are greeted by Angel Volunteers in Blue. They are there to assist you, giving you directions and making you feel welcome. We even started laughing for they thought my mother was the patient, and started to put her in the wheel chair.   They thought I looked "too good" to have the illness that I had.

The appointment I had at City of Hope took another positive turn during my meeting with Dr. Popplewell. Dr. Levine had mentioned a new targeted radiation therapy being tested at City of Hope for use in bone marrow transplants.   Dr. Popplewell told me about the Zevalin study.

The typical procedure to prepare your body for a bone marrow transplant is to have extended, whole body radiation to kill off the cancer cells. The side effects of whole body radiation can be horrific as it also kills off healthy cells.

Zevalin is an amazing discovery made by dedicated researchers searching for an alternative to full body radiation for bone marrow transplant recipients. Zevalin is a targeted Monoclonal Radioactive Antibody, a therapy used in combination with Rituxan, another targeted Monoclonal Antibody drug.

They work by attaching themselves to the cancer cells and releasing radiation to destroy them.   It doesn't render you weak, nor are there the devastating side effects of full body radiation.

Chemotherapy is still required, but with Zevalin, you are ready to face your next step in the transplant with more "fighting power," and strength, needed ingredient to move forward successfully when facing such an enormous battle.

I knew that with the Zevalin study, Dr. Popplewell and The City Of Hope was offering me a gift. I was willing and very ready to do what it took to get the best help available in the cancer research world. I was determined to to be cancer free.

There were just a few spaces left in the study, and I was told that I would have to qualify. The Bone Marrow Team, a group of highly experienced and dedicated professionals in the field of bone marrow transplants, came in to further explain what was involved in order to qualify for this golden opportunity. They were explicit in what is bone marrow and what are stem cells for what I was trying to qualify for was an Autologous Stem Cell Transplant; I would be using my own stem cells instead of getting cells from a donor or family member.

Bone marrow is the soft tissue inside some of your bones that contains immature cells, called stem cells. These stem cells develop into the red blood cells that carry oxygen through your body, the white blood cells that fight infections, and the platelets that help with blood clotting (due to my cancer, my white blood cells and platelets were abnormal). In a bone marrow transplant, you receive healthy stem cells after your bone marrow and blood cells (including any cancerous cells) have been destroyed by radiation and/or chemotherapy.   In a successful transplant, these healthy stem cells will multiply, and develop into new, healthy blood cells.

To receive a transplant of my own healthy stem cells, we would first have to harvest and collect them, in a process called Leukapheresis.   I would have to have a Central Venous Catheter placed surgically (I already had a porto-catheter; however it could not be used to siphon off cells).

After my cells were harvested, I would undergo a month long series of tests to see if my body was a match for the Zevalin study.   These tests involved small, test doses of Zevalin, an infusion of Rituxan, and multiple nuclear medicine scans, blood draws, continued urine collections, a chest X-ray, EKG, and lung air capacity tests, to determine how the targeted drugs spread through my body, and how I responded. If the results were not as expected, or I had a negative reaction, I would not be a candidate for the study. I would not receive Zevalin. I would have to endure full body radiation.

Little did I know that qualifying for this amazing progressive targeted therapy was going to be more difficult than getting into a top rated University.

TRAVEL GUIDE TIPS

• *Your level of anxiety can skyrocket during this very trying and frightening period. Speak to your doctor as to whether or not you need medication to help calm you down. Learn how to relax during the car ride to hospital - whether music helps, should the driver travel more slowly if he/she is a fast driver. Sometimes taking a "comfort" pillow, blanket or favorite stuffed animal for the ride can help calm you down.*

• *Make sure you have a convenient calendar for your purse and one at home for keeping track of all your appointments. Also make sure your designated partner knows what all appointments are. You have some control regarding time of appointments - think about if you are a morning or afternoon person...or if you will have to fast prior to a test.*

• *Set up a file or notebook to store all the paperwork you receive (guidelines, directions for tests, info on side effects, what to do in case of an emergency). Keep it easily accessible so you can refer back to it.*

CHAPTER 12

ENTERING A NEW ATMOSPHERE

"The great thing in this world is not so much where we are, but in what direction we are moving."

Oliver Wendell Holmes

I only wanted to go forward, and be given this unbelievable chance of being cured, and living.

With no time to waste, I started the beginning of the medical tests necessary to proceed within 24 hours. Fortunately, I was allowed to use Hoag Hospital Labs which were closer to my home for some of the tests (reaching City of Hope without traffic took over and hour and a half, one way. Hoag Hospital was forty minutes from my home).

On September 1st, 2004 my "Road to Recovery" started at City of Hope. Little did I know what would be totally involved. However, little did I care. How can one measure this miraculous opportunity?

I WANTED TO LIVE AT ALL COSTS...NO MATTER WHAT IT TOOK.

With fierce determination, never looking back, I went forward, entering a world that paralleled "An Alien Planet." The sounds, smells, even the attire that was worn by the professionals did not resemble the world I knew.

With all its strangeness, I understood that I had to focus, follow directions, and listen to those in charge.

The first goal I had to reach was going through the process of leukapheresis - accumulating and harvesting enough stem cells to proceed with the best chance possible of having a successful graft and transplant.

In order to collect these cells, I needed to have a central catheter line put in, which requires a surgical procedure.

Arrangements were initially made at Hoag Hospital to have this two pronged catheter placed in my chest. However, I am a strong advocate of "trusting your instincts." The doctor that I went to was totally unfamiliar with this particular hardware, and after seeing his confusion as to what it was I needed, I literally ran out of the office, with my mother quickly following me.

I also learned quickly that certain procedures I needed that related to my bone marrow transplant would be covered by insurance only if I used the physicians at City of Hope.

The day of my catheter surgery, I had the usual jitters. After meeting the surgeon, I felt more assured that all would be okay. After all, he did say to me that the biggest risk I would face with this type of catheter was having a collapsed lung. But in 99% of the cases who have this difficulty, the people are tall.

I breathed I sigh of relief, for after all, tall was not in my vocabulary. I am under five feet, vertically challenged. I am the woman who looks up at the item I need to purchase in a super market that is always on the top shelf, well beyond my reach.

I have always been one to solve my problems with a sense of humor. With a big smile on my face, I stop the tallest person I can find (preferably a good looking gentleman, after all one should have benefits if they have to humble themselves) and politely intro-duce myself as President of NASA - NATIONAL AS-SOCIATION OF SHORT ADULTS. I would appreciate his assistance to get the item I need down from the top shelf.

A few days after the placement of the central line, I had to start the procedure of receiving daily shots of Neupogen, which would increase my stem cell counts. The side effects are difficult to handle. Your bones ache, your body feels sore. I had to receive 14 straight days of those injections.

Leukapheresis (cell harvesting) started right af-ter completing my injections. I had to be driven daily to City of Hope's special lab where this procedure took place.

At the time, the lab had about 14 stations, each station had a patient, hooked up to a huge metallic machine that was siphoning out their blood; then going through the process of counting how many stem cells were accumulated for that day.

I was told prior to my "hook up" that the amount of cells I needed to have in order for me to successfully go forward with the best chances at a successful transplant was between 3-5 million. There was no real predicting how long it would take to accumulate that cell count, their educated guess was it could take anywhere from a week to 14 days...perhaps more.

I was silently saying a prayer to myself that I would have all the cells I needed in one week. Aside from my going through this unbelievable journey, Fred, lovingly called "My Supreme Saint" as his husband duties were now multiplied by 100 by being my caretaker, had to drive me back and forth to the hospital. That amounted to over three hours daily spent in the car and traffic. At the time, we were both simultaneously involved with "construction". I was building a "new healthy body" and he was in the midst of building a law office close to where we lived.

My prayers seemed to be working. The very first day, I was told by the lab that I accumulated one million stem cells. I was thrilled beyond words. It felt like I had won the lottery.

Having met with initial success, I felt mentally invigorated. I could nail this challenge. The second day I also accumulated another large amount. On the fifth day, I MADE IT...I HAD ACCUMULATED OVER THREE MILLION CELLS!

Those days were filled with challenging moments, from having nausea from having to eat a special calcium candy to support my body's depletion of cells, to having bowel problems.

One of the most embarrassing moments I encountered during this time was that after four days of being "clogged," I had the urge to go right in the middle of my being hooked up to the "blood machine."

My only option was to use a port-a-potty that would be positioned next to my bed (I was not allowed to unhook the lines).

My bed was located in the middle of the lab. To the right of me was a lovely young man (who was there over two weeks for he still hadn't accumulated enough of the necessary blood cells needed) and to the right of me was a dapper looking older gentleman. The only privacy I would have was the white curtain which surrounded me (made of material you could see through).

At first I did everything to NOT GO. I tried holding my legs closely together, trying to use visualization, singing to myself, anything to get my mind off my body, but I was unable to hold back "Nature" calling to me. I yelled for the nurse just in the nick of time.

She quickly helped me onto the portable toilet. As she scurried to pull the curtains around me, I DE-LIVERED!

Needless to say, aside from my pushing, groaning and moaning, everything was "not coming up roses." The smell alone could have knocked out the entire lab filled with over 14 patients.

I was beyond embarrassment. Yet I will never forget the kindness of the young man next to me who sensed how I felt.

He laughingly said he understood, for he too had a similar experience. He made a very uncomfortable situation for me so much more bearable. His being able to relate to me also reminded me that there was a feeling of "unity" in the lab. All of us were there for the one purpose of fighting for our lives. Embarrassing moments like these were so insignificant compared to the largeness of our goal.

The harvesting of my cells took five days in all. I started on a Monday, and ended on a Friday. I was thrilled to have the weekend off, although I was quite exhausted. The last day of my collection, it took over four hours to get home from the hospital...there was a total stand still on the freeway. There was a strange bag left alone next to a bench in the train station, adjacent to the freeway. The police had intervened, suspecting a possible terrorist act. All I cared about at that moment was just that I wanted to go home, be in my bed and left alone.

I did get what I wished for, but my moment of tranquility ended on the following Monday. I woke up in the morning with a horrific pain in my chest, and an inability to breathe normally. I convinced myself that I was just having an anxiety attack. After all I couldn't be having a collapsed lung for as the doctor said, I was short, and only tall people are at risk of a collapsed lung.

My darling mother, who was consistently at my side, knew only one thing...CHICKEN SOUP...THE CURE OF ALL AILMENTS. She decided that I was weak and she would bring me home made chicken soup at lunchtime. By the time she arrived, I could barely walk. Being the actress that I am (also knowing that I was going to City of Hope the following day to have my central line removed which I was determined to have out no matter what) I told my mother I was feeling better.

I might be an actress, but I could never fool my sister Betty, my hero. She came over too, took one look at me, measured my breaths per minute, and firmly told me to get in the car. We were going to the hospital.

I couldn't breathe, so I didn't argue. I was fearful that not only did I have a collapsed lung, I had an emboli, a blood clot. The drive up PCH towards Hoag Hospital was one of the most frightening rides in my life. I was convinced I was going to die. Intertwined with that emotion, I was fearful of being admitted to the hospital again. I was on overload. I'd had enough of hospitals. I just wanted to be home.

Entering Hoag Hospital, facing the familiar admissions office, I was hysterically crying. Yet there is humor with every crisis. Betty, who felt so badly for me and was equally terrified that I was in severe danger, along with her husband who was trying to calm me down, pushed me so quickly in the wheel chair, that they pushed me into a cement hospital wall by accident. On top of crying, I couldn't stop laughing.

I was immediately rushed to the lab where they did a special chest x-ray to see if I had a collapsed lung or had thrown an emboli. Sitting in that waiting room, I had bouts of crying and shaking. I was truly worn out.

There is no time to let your guard down in that situation. You always have to be prepared for the unexpected. When you think you have no emotional or physical strength left to face another challenge, you miraculously rise to the occasion.

I was placed on a bed next to a specific lung x-ray machine. The technician politely told me that with all the hardware I had in my body, the central line and the porto- catheter, that he couldn't use either one of them to access a vein. He needed a large vein to inject dye in to get the appropriate reading, therefore he had to start a new IV.

I had no workable veins left. After his third try, with tears running down my face from pain and frustration, he had to call in an IV Specialist. By the time they actually accessed my vein, I had been in the lab for over an hour and a half, and the IV nurse was successful after the eleventh try. I actually felt worse for them, than for myself. They truly felt so badly having put me through this medical nightmare that I told them, cheerleader I always am, they had earned the twelve Long Island ice teas I promised them as a reward for accessing my vein.

After the chest x-ray, more "waiting in the waiting room." We had been in the hospital for over seven hours. I was getting frantic, my imagination had taken over. I was sure I would be admitted and I would never be released in time to get my central line out (which was scheduled for noon the following day).

By eight o'clock that night my oncologist finally came by the waiting room with the results. He knew how badly I didn't want to be admitted and accommodated my request (not putting me in any danger). I did have a collapsed lung. With the proper antibiotics, I would not be at risk of infection (I had already had a few bouts of pneumonia).

By nine o'clock that night, I had a rendezvous with my husband at a most romantic location, a 24 hour CVS near my home (he had been in court all day not realizing what was happening until evening). My amazing sister and her wonderful husband kindly drove me to the drug store where we picked up my medicine. Needless to say, I was beyond exhausted. However, nothing stops me when I am determined to reach my goal. Tomorrow I was going to City of Hope and removing my central line.

The next day, after sleeping peacefully in my own bed, I had one of my dearest friends, who had stood by my side since the beginning of my illness, take me to City of Hope with my mother (who was slightly up-set that I was even going considering the amount of pain I was in due to my collapsed lung).

When I got to City of Hope, I once again had dif-ficulties walking on my own two feet. My friend, who understood how important it was for me to be free of the dreaded hardware, pushed me in a wheel chair up to the elevator. Then, by sheer determination, I walked into the unit to get my line out.

How I managed that day I will never know. With a fake smile hiding the grimace of my pained face, I told the doctor I was just fine and ready to be free of the line. She did suspect that I wasn't being totally honest, especially since my blood pressure was very elevated (I told her my spiked blood pressure was due to white coat syndrome - a patient's disease from seeing too many white lab coats). She removed my line.

FREE AT LAST, FREE AT LAST, FREE AT LAST...IT IS THE SMALL THINGS IN LIFE THAT BECOME THE BIG MEANINGFUL THINGS...I was coming closer and closer to getting back to being just me, without any foreign implantations (or so I thought).

TRAVEL GUIDE TIPS

• *If you are having blood tests- make sure you drink plenty of water, hydration helps make your veins easier to access. If you have a porto-catheter, advise the nurse of your needle size, and ways that are comfortable for you to be accessed (Emla cream helps numb the area).*

• *Make sure you have snacks and water in the car, you need to stay hydrated. There are some drugs that cause nausea, crackers help. If you think you might get sick, have anti-nausea drugs readily available. Paper bags / emersion basins do help.*

• *Get familiar with sanitary and easily available bathrooms on your journey. There is nothing worse than looking for a bathroom and you can't find one!!*

• *Use your time during your treatments or hospitalization as a "Spiritual Journey." Provide yourself with reading materials that will help your own personal growth and development; bring you comfort, motivation, inspiration and hope. See my list of suggested reading material at the end of this book.*

CHAPTER 13

HOPE

"Hope is a thing with feathers,
that perches on the soul."

Emily Dickinson

City of Hope contacted me right after the removal of my central line saying the time was now to proceed with my transplant schedule. Being in action mode suited me, I was ready to move forward and resume with life. I was envisioning myself and my life back the way things had been, including going back to the classroom.

I went to City of Hope the day before the "Action" to be tested to see if I was an acceptable candidate for receiving Zevalin. I was determined to receive this type of radiation as I believed my body would have the best chance at eradicating those unwelcome diseased cells, without damaging the cells that were healthy (Zevalin was showing great results statistically). I also knew, based on my research, that having whole body radiation is brutal.

On Wednesday, September 1, 2004 (Day 28 according to the transplant schedule countdown) I started by picking up the contrast dye I would drink for my CAT SCAN. On September 3rd, I had my CAT SCAN (those drinks were quite awful. I used to make believe that they were Apple Martinis...my favorite...I even nicked name the drinks at City Of Hope Martinis...it made the other patients smile and enabled us all to swallow the chalky tasteless drinks more easily). Tuesday, September 7th, I had to have a PET SCAN (now modern technology has advanced so you have a PET/CAT SCAN simultaneously, and drink a much tastier drink one hour prior to testing).

On September 8th, countdown day 21, I received my Rituxan infusion (the targeted therapy with super results), had blood drawn, and received a nuclear scan (quite difficult, you have to remain in a still position holding your hands above your head for 45 minutes straight). I was sent home with a large orange container to start my urine collection.

Every day for the next week, I was to visit City of Hope to receive a nuclear medicine scan each to see if Zevalin liked me.

Going back and forth to City of Hope was emotionally taxing. I wanted to "make it," to get the green light that I was "in." During that time, I used to think how hard it must be for students who want to make their university of choice, do what it takes, yet, due to circumstances or despite their efforts, they are rejected.

Despite the traveling back and forth, life does go on. On the third day of my weekly urine collection (I had to pee into a cup every time I went to the bathroom, then transfer it into a large orange container that I would turn in on Tuesday, September 14th when I received my last nuclear scan), Fred and I arranged a date to meet with our very close friends at a beautiful restaurant which was located 30 minutes from my home.

Wanting to be out and about, NOT IN A HOSPITAL ENVIRONMENT, I had to figure out how I would collect my urine. Not going to the bathroom was not an option. I also knew that the orange container, which was getting quite heavy, had to go with me. How was I going to be discrete regarding this medical situation I was in?

I had my "Aha" moment while I was looking through my closet to see what I was going to wear. Amongst my purses, I had a very large plastic traveling bag, with pictures of suitcases on it. I ran to see if the orange container would fit in, along with my urine cup. Lo and behold, I could disguise my equipment "in style"! I even matched my outfit to the bag.

When we arrived at the restaurant, I quietly explained to my dear friend that I might need her help when I had to go to the bathroom. After explaining to her my situation, we both started to hysterically laugh.

She knows nothing can hold me back when I decide I want to do something, even "peeing into a bottle."

We had a lovely time, for that moment I actually felt part of the "normal world" where people walk around in colorful clothing, without IV lines coming out of their arms. Then, reality hit. Fred noticed my large purse (some men are not strong in the observation department), and offered to hold it for me. Before I could even say no, he took the bag holding all my urine that I collected for three days.

Need I say, he was quite shocked at the heaviness of my bag. He is used to seeing me carry a heavy purse, but he had never experienced this type of dead weight.

He looked at me inquisitively, asking me what is it that I have in my bag? All I could do was laugh and say "you wouldn't believe it if I told you."

After discovering the contents of my bag, he broke into laughter. Sharing the information with our friends, laughing at what we were holding, truly lightened up a most difficult challenge. That night was medicinal for me, the levity is what I needed and helped prepare me for what I was about to face.

SEPTEMBER 14TH -DOES SHE OR DOESN'T SHE MAKE IT INTO THE STUDY??

Tuesday, September 14, 2008 turned out to be another life altering day.

I was instructed to show up at City of Hope at 8:00 a.m. for my final nuclear medicine scan to see the last results of the injected Zevalin sample. I was to bring my huge orange container of urine (I almost needed a hand crane it was so heavy), and a suitcase packed for a potential stay of at least three days - if I was accepted into the Zevalin study, I be admitted to the hospital that evening, and prepped to receive my first full dose of Zevalin the following morning.

My sister and my brother-in-law drove me to City of Hope (Fred was in court, if I was hospitalized that day, he was going to visit me later on).

In all, the final scan procedures took about three hours, I was done at 11:00 am. The doctors would be meeting at 2:00 p.m. to review my results, evaluate my case, and make their decision. At 3:00 p.m. they would deliver their verdict and telephone me; Zevalin Study for Michelle Pardes "yea or nay."

That meant FOUR HOURS OF WAITING FOR ONE OF THE MOST IMPORTANT DECISIONS IN MY LIFE - AND I HAD NO CONTROL OVER IT!

Waiting around the locale of City of Hope, especially on a day that was brutally hot, can be quite taxing. There is only so much eating and/or shopping one can do. I was too nervous to actually eat, and believe it or not, I couldn't focus on buying anything.

We had rented a motel room a few blocks away from City of Hope in Duarte. In case I was hospitalized my husband would be staying over night. The Zevalin procedure was scheduled for the following day, Fred would be by my side.

My anxious and drained sister and brother-in-law did their best to distract and entertain me. We went to Pasadena, ate at a great Brazilian restaurant. But you can only sit and eat so much, especially when you are preoccupied. My only thoughts were about what time it was and how much longer it was to 3:00 P.M. After lunch, we drove around looking at very pretty homes and hills around the Duarte vicinity. I was totally uninterested. We entered the motel at 1:00 p.m.

TWO HOURS. I HAD 120 MINUTES TO WAIT FOR A PHONE TO RING.

Waiting to hear the sweet sound of the phone, with hopefully good news on the other end, reminded me of the times I used to wait by my phone as a teenager. How strange. I remember feeling jumpy and impatient. I wouldn't leave the phone just in case it would ring and I wasn't there to answer it (I am certainly dating myself, we didn't have voice machines/call waiting then).

Everything is relative. I felt then that my whole world would fall apart if the boy I liked didn't call me like he promised he would. Now, placed in another "waiting" scenario nearly 40 years later, the emotional feelings were familiar, but the level of importance was quite different.

There was one round old fashioned clock in the motel room. As I sat and tried to read a magazine to help pass the time, all I could do was stare at the clock. The more I stared at the clock the slower it appeared to go.

One minute lasted for ever.

No matter how slowly the clock appeared to go for me, time does move forward. After waiting a torturous two hours, the phone rang at exactly three o'clock. The research doctors, my oncologists, and other medical professionals who were on the team had met to decide who was to enter the study. Their decision was based on medical results and a psychological overview to determine if the person would be a viable candidate.

My heart was racing, beating so loudly, I could barely hear what was told to me by a most special nurse practitioner who played an important role in this study. She had to tell me over and over again, I MADE IT INTO THE ZEVALIN STUDY. She laughingly said, "who could ever say no to you?" My fierce determination and "joie de vivre" attitude certainly contributed to their decision.

At 5:00 o'clock that afternoon, I literally danced into the hallways of City of Hope. You would think I was going to a prom, the way I was dancing in the hallways of the hospital. I was filled with joy, happiness and lots of HOPE! The door had opened for me. I would go in, get the magic radiation therapy, get the bone marrow transplant. Voila...I would be done. My cancer would be gone.

The following morning, after receiving another infusion of Rituxan, having my blood drawn, and collecting more urine into my infamous orange container, I was wheeled into a special lab where Dr. Andrew Raubitschek, Specialty, Cancer - Immunotherapeutics and Tumor Immunology, was waiting for me. He was the incredible researcher who was going to give me the infusion of Zevalin.

Aside from looking like a very kind gentleman, he turned out to be one of the most amazing storytellers I have ever met in my life. As a fellow storyteller, we were so engaged with the humorous conversations of his life and mine, that little attention was paid to his hand made wooden and metal device that delivered Zevalin to me.

The moment that I thought would be so tense, was just the opposite. In a way, the bigness of the situation was almost impossible to process. I was still laughing when I remember asking Dr. Raubitchek what is it that his wife does? His response was that she was a clown. I couldn't believe it. He explained that she became a clown to bring joy to those who needed laughter in their lives (since then I have met three people who have become clowns...sounds like a great profession...maybe I will put becoming a clown on my own personal bucket list). My "Supreme Saint" husband was in the room with me, still appearing tense, yet he too, shared in the laughing from Dr. Raubitchek's stories.

After completing the Zevalin infusion, I was placed in solitary confinement in a small room with lead coating and a very tiny window. The room reminded me of a room "Superman" would need if he was exposed to Kryptonite. Anyone that came in had to use special precautions due to the highly radioactive person walking around that room - little old me. I kept humming "You light up my life, you give me hope to carry on." I certainly was "glowing."

I would spend the next 3 to 4 days in solitary, depending on how long it took the radiation to clear sufficiently from my body. When my radioactivity was considered within "safety range limits," I'd be released from the hospital while the Zevalin worked it's magic. Then I'd returning for the massive dose of chemo that would effectively kill me, preparing me for my transplant rebirth.

On the third day of my solitary hospitalization, I had an acceptable radioactivity reading. Yes, they used a Geiger counter to measure the rays I was emitting. I was allowed to go home on September 18th. I was still receiving nuclear scans.   On my 53rd birthday, September 20th, my special friend and her darling father took me back to City of Hope for another round of scans.   She really tried so hard to make me laugh while I was in "position" inside the scan machine.   I don't know how I had the will power to not burst out laughing.

I was still traveling to and from City of Hope that week. Included in the protocol prior to the actual transplant I had to have a bone marrow biopsy. Luckily, I learned quickly that I needed sedation to survive the horrific pain of that procedure.

Traditionally, this time of the year we are engaged in going to synagogue for the Jewish holidays. This year, tradition was put on a back burner. I was slightly depressed I wouldn't be with my family.

My wonderful son David came in from out of town (I was fortunate I had my other special son Jonathan living here with us.) My dear daughter was living with her husband on the other side of the United States in Burlington, Vermont.   Due to my body still being somewhat radioactive, my adult children had to keep at least 10 feet away from me (exposure to radiation if you are of child bearing age is not recommended).   My dear friend, who is so scientifically knowledgeable, actually had a Geiger counter, and I can proudly say that I did trigger it!

The clock kept ticking, my scheduled bone marrow transplant was getting closer and closer.

On Friday Night, September 24th, on one of the holiest nights in the Jewish faith, Kol Nidre (the night service before Yom Kippur, Day of Atonement was the following day), I was admitted to the Bone Marrow Transplant Unit. I was packed, ready to get on with the show; waiting can truly get you jittery.

After my family dropped me off, I started to feel so sad. I was always with my family during the holidays. I will never forget the "forever gift" Fred gave me. While I was in the hospital, he called me from Temple, and held up his phone so I could hear the sweet sounds of the blowing of the Shofar. For that one minute I was actually transported back, standing next to him, sharing the tradition that goes back thousands of years.

I promised if I survived that I would personally stand in front of the Shofar Blower every year, never forgetting how blessed and grateful I am to be alive.

As I write this book, I HAVE BEEN IN FRONT OF THE SHOFAR BLOWER FOR SEVEN YEARS, NEVER FORGETTING THE GIFT OF LIFE I HAVE BEEN BLESSED WITH.

TRAVEL GUIDE TIPS

• *Set your daily goals and plans. Post them where you can see them clearly. Stay Focused.*

• *Remember to include daily laughter in your plan. Read the daily funny comic strips, watch comedy on TV, read joke books, see a funny movie. "Humor makes all things tolerable." Henry Ward Beecher*

• *Try to be sensitive to your caretaker(s) feelings. It is equally as hard for the person caring for you, as it is for you having to ask for care. Try to be gracious.*

• *Try to be creative in situations that can take away your ability to go on and enjoy your daily life activities. Learn to adapt and adjust.*

• *"Attitudes are contagious. Do you want people around you to catch yours?" Bob Moaward. Even though you are facing enormous physical and psychological challenges, try to put your best foot forward. Plant a smile on your face even when you don't feel like it around those that love you.*

CHAPTER 14

REBIRTH

"Change is the constant, the signal for re-birth, the egg of the phoenix"

Christina Baldwin

On the Day of Atonement, when Jews all over the world are praying for forgiveness, and fasting, I too, was doing the same, expect in a different way and format.

On Saturday, September 25th, I received my first dose of extremely painful chemotherapy, Etoposide. Your mouth feels like you have one hundred candles burning inside of it. The pain is blinding. The nurses do the best they can to "put out the fires of pain" by using medication and continually making you suck on popsicles.

I had a roommate in the room with me for the first round of chemotherapy. She was so very brave, trying so hard to manage this horrific pain. She tried talking with me intermittently while we were having the infusion.

What I will never forget about her was due to her insurance and other medical reasons, she was not accepted into the Zevalin study. She was also well researched and was convinced that this targeted therapy would add to the success of the bone marrow transplant. She knew I had been accepted into the study. She expressed her frustration and sadness (she was in her late 50's) for she believed her cancer would still remain evident without the additional boost of Zevalin. She died a year after her bone marrow transplant.

On Sunday, I had my day of rest. The mind is a wonderful thing. The outstanding pain I felt receiving the chemotherapy the day before had disappeared. I was feeling better. But not for long.

On Monday, September 27th, I received a "major Chemo Punch." I was given an infusion of Cyclophosphamide. What I thought was difficult on my first round of chemotherapy two days before was nothing compared to this. The pain is indescribable. My mouth was on fire, it felt as if I had drank one hundred cups of scalding hot coffee. The nurses, along with my special Angels, my sister and brother-in-law, brought me popsicles every few minutes to provide relief. Even now, I actually start shaking at the thought of going through that moment.

MOMENT- what may seem like forever is just a moment. As my father always said, "No pain, No gain."

Somehow, you do make it through the very worst of times. No matter what, I was still in the frame of mind that I was willing to experience any hardship as long as the result would be successful.

Another 24 hour round of chemotherapy was given to me on Wednesday, September 29th, my husband's birthday. At least he was at City of Hope on a significant day, Lance Armstrong was there, kicking off his ride across the United States bringing cancer awareness and his most important message to LIVE STRONG to others. At this point, all my blood cells had been destroyed, I was left with O cells...no immune system. After the few days of chemotherapy, my body was totally prepped to receive a transplant of my own stem cells.

That day, according to the City of Hope transplant calendar was called Day Zero. My rebirth, my receiving of healthy new cells was to happen the next day, September 30th. The peripheral stem cell re-infusion, Day 1, was really going to happen. A chance at life. A chance that the cancer I had been battling for so long was going to be destroyed. The thought was so unbelievable.

AT THIS EXACT MOMENT OF MY WRITING THIS BOOK, I AM OFFICIALLY SIX YEARS OLD. WHAT AN AMAZING WAY TO CELEBRATE THIS BIRTHDAY...WRITING AND PAYING FORWARD LESSONS AND TIPS I LEARNED, TO HELP OTHERS

WHO ARE TRAVELING OR WILL TRAVEL ON A SIMILAR PATH OF LIFE CHALLENGES.

The day had arrived where the five small glass vials that held my precious stem cells were going to be given to me through my IV. The moment was too big to even appreciate. I remember my sister was fearful that there would be an earthquake and the containers that held my cells would be dropped and destroyed. Once you harvest your cells, you can no longer have that procedure again.

My husband, equally excited at the concept of my "infusion of life," and wanting to support me through this procedure, was allowed to come into the room where I was going to have my "rebirth."

Everyone was on edge, including me, and poor Fred witnessed a close call that undid him. The nurse who was removing the cap from one of the five vials which held my cells (that is it folks...you can't lose a drop of those cells...there is no do over!) dropped the vial. As the tube was slowly falling to the ground, it was miraculously caught by someone who had extremely quick hands.

Quick hands. Quick fear. Fred was terrified and enraged. He had to leave the room, he was too emotional to watch. His nerves were shattered (but better his nerves than the vial of my cells).

Pushing the cells into my IV was not comfortable. Luckily I was heavily sedated so my memory of that moment is unclear, but I do remember how slowly they allowed them to go into me. I felt some pain, but more importantly I remember feeling extremely cold. I was shivering internally. I remember wanting to just feel a sense of warmth. The feeling of cold lasted quite a while. My very close friend remembers calling me right after my infusions and I was screaming that I was freezing. You never can imagine feeling that level of coldness.

The number nine is very important when one is giving birth (we carry our babies 9 months in a full term pregnancy). My own rebirth, where the cells graft and begin to grow in my bone marrow, took nine days.

I have absolutely no recollection of those days, I was heavily drugged on Dilaudid, an opium base narcotic. I wish I could say the same for Fred. Those nine days, waiting to see if my transplant was going to be successful, if I would I live or die, my husband paced and waited to see if those cells would start my healthy life again. I can't imagine what he or my family went through.

On the ninth day, my wonderful oncologist announced to Fred that the bone marrow transplant was a success. My blood cell count was 320. I had grown 320 new cells! Through my drug haze I was able to see that number next to Day 9 on the board. My dream was becoming a reality. I was "Still Breathing", Still Alive!

I remember starting to come around at Day 12. I wanted to see my mother and my sister (Fred had been the only one allowed there for I had no immune system).

After pleading with the doctors, my mother and sister were allowed to visit me. I still remember the disbelief I felt that they were standing in front of me. I became quite emotional.

From that point on, my mother, sister and my husband visited me daily. Besides being challenged by the lengthy ride to get there, Fred was still in the midst of construction of his professional building, and my sister had to juggle her work schedule in order to visit me.

While my blood cells were multiplying, so were my many new challenges. I was on tube feedings...I hated the smell. I had so many IV lines hooked on my body. I was extremely weak. I also was exhausted from being poked and prodded. I was disoriented. I couldn't tell day from night. I remember how I hated the feeling of the sun setting and I saw darkness outside my window.. I felt the most alone during that time.

City of Hope Social Services provided psychological support during the healing process of having a transplant. A young male social worker intern was assigned to me. He was to listen, comfort, advise and support me during this challenging time. I believe I was the first bone marrow transplant patient he ever worked with. He was terribly nervous counseling me.

I felt so sorry for him. I did everything to make him feel comfortable and successful. However, I had difficulty keeping a straight face, when he repeated his favorite statement, "there are peaks and valleys in life...you have to prepare to go up and down emotionally."

The room I was in was quite small and there was no extra chair (now City of Hope has a brand new state of the art Lymphoma Building). The counselor always decided to sit on my bathroom commode. I have never been counseled before or since by anyone sitting on a toilet. I do hope he is still professionally involved in assisting patients to overcome their obstacles when they are having life altering medical procedures. Hopefully he is sitting on a chair or couch when talking to his clients.

My experience at City of Hope was not only a life altering event medically, it was a life altering event emotionally.

When one goes on a strict food diet, and we are prohibited to eat certain foods, somehow all we think about are the foods that we can't eat.

Being placed in isolation due to my condition was something I was truly unprepared for. You can be warned of your restrictions and told what you are facing by many professionals, yet until you experience the feeling of being "locked up" it is unimaginable.

You also begin to feel enslaved by the multiple IV lines that you are attached to. At the very beginning of the transplant, my body was being sustained and nourished through tubes. I remember looking at the tube that was the "food" line. I kept thinking about just tasting one bite of real food, the smell of a steak on the barbeque grill, spaghetti with tomato sauce, veal parmigiana, or my favorite, a Nathan's hot dog with lots of sauerkraut, and crinkled french fries with tons of ketchup. Despite my very vivid imagination, that thick yellow "mush" traveling through tubes attached to my body was what I had for breakfast, lunch and dinner.

Another thing that I was craving was being outside, smelling the grass, flowers, and feeling warm rays of sunshine on my face.

I couldn't wait until I could be ambulatory, get out of bed, and move. Just the thought of being able to go to the bathroom by myself, and take a shower without anything protruding out of my body was what I dreamed about and hoped for.

Seeing people outside a hospital environment, talking to people without wearing cotton striped or blue gowns, wearing face masks, hugging someone without the worry of being contaminated or fear that one of their germs would affect me medically was something I also fantasized about.

I could actually hear my father talk to me about what he felt like being in a concentration camp, not having the small luxuries of life, holding on faithfully to the belief that there would be a time he would be a free man, again able to enjoy the beauty that life has to offer.

I could hear him say to me, "Michykoo [his nick-name for me], be patient, do what you have to do to get well, be disciplined with your body and mind and you will be successful." Not only did he understand what it took to survive in the worst possible circumstances, he also knew how to survive in hospital settings for he had been in and out of one during his own battle with leu-kemia. He was so disciplined, making exercise his pri-ority in order to gain his strength back.

By my third week post transplant, I was deter-mined to return home and recover there. I couldn't have realized this goal with out the love and support of my family and close friends who wanted to honor my wishes. However, I still had to gain more strength and stamina to be able to help make this possibility a reality.

I will never forget the very first time I was al-lowed outside. I was attached to a very large IV machine with multiple lines attached to me. My mother and sister walked slowly with me, leading me to the door that had held me captive for so many weeks. I couldn't wait to go outside and breathe the fresh air.

My mother and sister walked me over to a picnic area, and we sat under a tree, adjacent to the most beautiful rose garden. An act that I would have not given a thought about in the past, simply walking 100 yards, was an enormous accomplishment for me at that time.

While I was outside with my family I loved seeing people going about their business, getting in and out of cars, people drinking coffee...living LIFE. I started to feel reconnected to the human race. I felt alive.

The effect of being outside was overwhelming that day. I was struck by the color of the sky, I never realized how blue it was. The sensation of the breeze on my skin was unbelievable. And seeing the sun, this round, deep yellow ball, was breathtaking!

I will always remember the significance of leaving the sanctuary of the hospital that day and being allowed to taste life once again. What an incredible feeling. I promised myself then that I would never take our beautiful world we live in for granted.

Step by step I was being given back the luxuries of every day living I had missed so much. Right after the cathartic day when I saw the world we live in with my new eyes, I was given the green light to take a shower..

I will never forget the most wonderful nurse who came to assist me to take that first momentous shower. She helped me disrobe without pulling out my IV lines. She then carefully clamped the lines shut and disconnected them. For the first time in weeks I was no longer attached to anything. I was totally "me." No attachments.

She assisted me into the shower stall. At first she placed me under the shower head and turned the water on making sure the temperature was agreeable with me. I nearly collapsed for I was weaker than I realized. She was amazingly strong. She held me up so I could feel the water running down on me. That sensation was indescribable. The memory of that very first shower without "wires" will be forever imprinted in my brain.

When I got dressed after the shower I felt a burst of energy. I decided to take a walk alone. I was gaining confidence in being able to navigate "my attachments," they no longer were as cumbersome as I had less IV lines.

Leaving my room, I couldn't help but notice the person in the room next to mine. Lying in the bed was a young man, wearing a yarmulka (prayer covering) on his head. He was holding a siddur (a hebrew prayer book), deeply engaged in prayer, moving his lips silently.   Next to him, seated, was a young woman dressed formally in a long sleeve shirt and a long skirt.

He had the most serene peaceful look on his face. He must have sensed me looking at him - he looked up and greeted me with a smile.   He asked me sincerely, how was I doing?   I told him I felt wonderful just being up and able to walk about.   He once again smiled at me, nodding in agreement, that the feeling of standing on your own two feet is simply fantastic.

The young man asked me what I was there for, and I told him about my illness and my bone marrow transplant. He smiled again, and asked if it would be okay to say a "prayer of healing" for me.   I immediately said yes, thinking I too, would say a prayer for his healing when I returned home and attended synagogue.

With a fierce determined look, he lifted his thin weak arms, and recited "Mi Sheberakh," the traditional Jewish prayer for the sick; "May the One who blessed our ancestors bless and heal the one who is ill."   His face was shining with so much sincerity when he said it for me.   I thanked him profusely saying I would stop by tomorrow to visit and see how he was doing.

The next day came about, and as promised, I got up by myself, feeling stronger than the day before, and proceeded to put on my mask to be able to walk outside. I went straight to his room.

I looked into his room, and you could actually hear the silence. The bed was empty. The room had lost its personal look, no pictures on the wall, no books on the shelves. I couldn't understand or perhaps chose not to understand where he was.

A nurse who saw me staring into the room answered the question I was about to ask with her eyes first, then her voice followed. The young man, just twenty seven years old, had died during the night.

Here I was standing, much older than he was, having experienced so many wonderful things in my life; a wedding, marriage, children, experiencing joyful events and traveling to many countries. It just wasn't fair. Tears started running down my face.

I reflected back to how he looked when he was praying for me. Despite the fact that he knew how sick he was, he had demonstrated the feeling of joy with his loving smile as he prayed for me. That amazing act of kindness, which provided me with hope for a healthier and better tomorrow, has stayed with me until this very moment. I promised myself that I too, as this generous and loving man had shown me, would actively provide hope for those that are fighting for their lives.

Within a few days of his passing, I was being prepared to leave City of Hope, to return home and convalesce.

TRAVEL GUIDE TIPS

• *Pack items that will bring you a sense of comfort - your own blanket, pillow, stuffed animals, framed photos of your loved ones to put on your night stand. Seeing their faces will remind you how much you are loved and why you have to fight as hard as you can to heal.*

• *Being inside a hospital dries up your skin. Keep lip balm and lotion by your bed. Make sure your caretaker applies cream to the bottom of your feet, especially your heels.*

• *Try, with Doctor's permission, to move to a chair and eat out of bed. Not only is it good psychologically to be out of bed, it helps with your digestion.*

• *No matter how poorly you might be feeling, try to comb your hair or wig. If wearing a head scarf, try to make it comfortable and attractive on your head.*

• *Bring comfortable pajamas from home. Also bring a robe, and slippers. How you dress will help make you feel better. (I treated myself to some lovely flannel pajamas, and some cashmere head coverings to feel cuddly and look good).*

• *For those that like wearing make up, putting on a little lipstick and blush can spruce you up. (I was known as the Maybelline Queen).*

• *Check to see if your room has an internet connection. Being able to connect with the outside world using on line devices can help.*

• *Communicate your needs to the necessary medical personal. Don't assume they understand how you feel. The same goes for those that are involved with your care at home.*

• *When you are able to be ambulated, try to exercise by walking laps around the hallway. Some newer hospitals may have an exercise room or offer exercise bikes in your rooms.*

• *If allowed, see if you can have a light massage in the hospital or at home. It helps your healing on so many different levels.*

• *Make sure you let your feelings be known in advance how you feel about having visitors. In certain units, there are strict rules regarding this issue. Get the rest you need. Seeing too many people at one time can be overwhelming. Limit the amount of time you speak on the phone, it can get exhausting!*

• *Treats - if you are on a special diet, please be careful with what you can eat. Always check with the nurse or doctor before eating that special candy / cake that was delivered to you.*

• *If you have a problem with medical personnel make sure you address it using appropriate procedures. I did have a situation at City of Hope, was directed to the appropriate person and the issue was handled expeditiously.*

• *Reading materials, music and iPods. help.. Also listening to books on tape can be entertaining.*

• *Having the appropriate Hospital Chaplain or your own Professional Persons of your own faith come to pray with you can be helpful and healing.*

• *Remember, that as hard as it is to be a patient in a hospital, as Annie in the play sang in her beautiful song "Tomorrow," hang onto your tomorrows...it will get better!*

CHAPTER 15

INPUT OVERLOAD

"The wisest mind has something yet to learn."

George Santayana

Exiting City of Hope three weeks post my bone marrow transplant was surreal. I went through the motions of packing up all my belongings.

Looking at what I brought to the hospital, I realized I'd had absolutely no clue of what my needs were going to be as a patient in a Bone Marrow Transplant Unit. I was truly delusional.

I actually thought I would have leisurely hours while I was "healing" to catch up on my reading. I packed so many books I could have started my own personal library in my hospital room!

I DIDN'T READ ONE BOOK.

Due to my physiological limitations, extreme weakness and malaise, I didn't have the strength to even hold a book up in the beginning. I also had no focusing ability due to all the drugs I was on.

I had been given many wonderful gifts to occupy the time while I was in the hospital; i.e. crossword puzzle books, embroidery sets, art sets, word search books, numbers games. While I loved the thoughtful gestures, I didn't touch them at all during my stay.

I'd packed a laptop computer. The only time I used it was when Fred showed me photos of my children and friends who were attending a wedding at Cape Cod.

Seeing my adult children there without their mother and father in the photos was devastating to me. All I could do was cry. The reality of where I was was staring me in the face. My heart was truly broken. The thought that I would ever again attend fun events, laugh or be merry was inconceivable to me. My poor husband thought he would be cheering me up by sharing this moment with me using technology.

I brought street clothes to the hospital thinking I would be able to "dress normally" once I was ambulatory. WRONG! I only wanted to wear warm and snugly things like the flannel pajamas for they brought me comfort. This type of attire is also easier to manage when "nature is calling" - bathroom assistance wasn't always available when I needed it and I had many "oops" and embarrassing moments.

It was finally time for me to leave the hospital and go home. Once again, I played The Waiting Game. I had to wait for the discharge staff nurse to bring and review all the paper work for my release, including directions I needed to follow at home regarding handling isolation, medications, and wearing a mask whenever I left the house (getting used to wearing a cover over my mouth was so difficult, especially in the department of breathing).

After all the business you have to take care of is complete, you have to wait for an orderly to bring you a wheel chair...hospital policy. Packing lightly has never been my strength, so aside from the wheel chair I needed, I also had to have three carts to load up my belongings.

I had an entourage leaving the hospital with me. Fred was carrying all my blankets and pillows I brought from home, and two orderlies pushed the carts and me out the doors to FREEDOM!

There was a sense of excitement felt by all those "Angels," doctors, nurses, nurses aids, and staff as I was being liberated. I had convinced them that if I survived the bone marrow transplant, I was going buy my fantasy car, a white Jaguar!

Little did I know, Fred, "The Supreme Saint," planned to take me directly to the Jaguar dealership. He felt that after what I had been through I deserved to have anything I wanted. If I wanted this car, so be it, I would have this car.

The funny thing is that what I'd once thought was important no longer held the same value for me.

We did go to the Jaguar dealership. I did sit in the white Jaguar, wearing a white mask and outside hospital attire. At first, I was on such a high, my dream was going to coming true. But what I thought was my dream in the hospital had been replaced by something much more significant than a car. I HAD SURVIVED! I WAS GOING HOME WITH MY HUS-BAND! I WOULD BE AMONGST MY FAMILY AND FRIENDS.

Fred was anxiously waiting for me to nod my head yes to confirm that this was the car I wanted. He looked totally shocked when I shook my head no and left the car.

I explained to him that when I sat in the car I re-alized that it did not hold the same meaning for me it had in the hospital. The bigger prize was that I was outside, breathing air, living, dressed in street clothes and very much alive. You can't get better than that.

So off I went, no Jaguar, but feeling I'd won the real lottery. I was heading home with my loved ones, "Still Breathing."

What I had fantasized every second I was lucid in the hospital...TO BE HOME! FINALLY HOME! "There's no place like home, there's no place like home" - Dorothy, from The Wizard of Oz.

I once again did not realize the multiple challenges I was going to face "re-entering" back into an environment that I thought was so familiar to me.

Plans had been made for me to have a live-in caretaker. Based upon my needs and previous history of what it is like to care for someone full time, my husband, mother, sister, and brother-in-law (Michelle's Health Team) decided it was best for someone to be with me full time, monitoring my health (I went home with a cough that had to be watched so it didn't turn into pneumonia), keeping me clean, keeping the house sterile, doing the necessary cooking and household upkeep.

I had another amazing team headed by my very close friends, who had come into the house prior to my arrival to entirely clean out my refrigerator and pantry. They reviewed what items were past their due dates and whether the foods would be safe to eat. I don't think they ever forgot how "white" my refrigerator really was. There was absolutely nothing inside of it, except for a jar of pickles and one can of soda. My husband proudly boasted to them that while I was gone he hadn't eaten one cooked meal at home, he had fine dinning each night...Taco Bell, McDonalds, Carl's Jr. and In and Out Burgers.

My mother brought my new caretaker, Tess (who truly turned out to be the most amazing, caring super caretaker), and my wonderful cleaning lady Sylvia and her crew to thoroughly clean and sterilize my house.

Being that I had to stay in a more sterile environment that was kept as germ free as possible, arrangements were made for me to sleep solo in the guest bedroom on the other side of my house. Tess, my caretaker would be staying adjacent to me in her own room. My gray cheeked parrot, Sunny, was given away. All houseplants were removed from our home. An air filtration system was put in to provide additional support to help keep my living environment as germ free as possible.

Last but not least, there were jars of disinfectant liquid placed in every room, to be used by all who came into the house. Simply looking at what it took to keep me healthy and germ free was unbelievable.

The house I came home to from City of Hope post bone marrow transplant was certainly not like the home I left. I felt so out of place, truly off balanced. Everything was so topsy turvy...I did not expect these feelings at all!!

The next few weeks, the "period of adjustment" were very difficult for me. I went from being a person dependent on IVs to a person dependent on my caretaker, close family and friends. I was disoriented, feeling exhausted all the time.

I had craved to be in the sun, yet I was not allowed direct sunlight due to my medical condition and pills I was taking. My first time outside with my sweet caretaker, I acted like a child, refusing to stay under the umbrella she held over my heard. I paid the price, I had a nasty sunburn the next day.

I also wanted to just go out anywhere, as long as it was not back to a hospital. Tess couldn't drive, so I was reliant on my friends just to take me to local stores. What I didn't realize was that seeing people wearing masks in hospitals was typical. But I was the only one wearing a mask when I was in a non-hospital environment. Being stared at takes some getting used to. Fortunately, my sense of humor worked in my favor. I got quite creative explaining the reason for my mask (Zorro and I could have related to one another).

Then, facing my everyday challenges. How do you fill up your day? I was so used to a life filled with so many personal and professional activities, I didn't know how just to "sit" and "chill out." Being the busy person I was, I'd never watched TV during the day time. I was a multi-tasker. How does a known "juggler of a multitude of tasks" adjust to having one focus...to heal and get well?

ME...MYSELF...I...

Learning to think only about myself was atypical for me. I had always been concerned about the well being of my immediate family, taking care of a husband, three children, extended family, friends and professional career (caring for the education of my students). Focusing on myself was foreign to me.

I FELT TOTALLY DISCONNECTED DURING THIS ADJUSTMENT TIME.

I went from wanting to jump back into the world that I knew to wanting to retreat. I didn't want to talk on the phone, I was tired of people asking me how I was, or commenting how lucky I was to be alive (I didn't need to be reminded of a fact that I knew, know and will always know the rest of my life). I was sick of hearing well meaning comments like "you are so lucky to have all this time on your hands" and "I would love to be home and just chill out."

How wrong everyone was. I was tormented for here I was alive, surviving the impossible while so many others that I knew died, yet I was miserable. I didn't know who I was...I had lost my identity, my MOJO.

Just a month before Thanksgiving, my younger son, Jonathan, took me for a check up at City of Hope. I had all my results in from the PET and CAT scans, and blood results for my afternoon consultation with my oncologist. Again, was I knocked down with the news she delivered to me. She told me that I still had a small tumor left in my abdominal area (my original tumor in that area was 17 cm's.) and I needed to have three weeks of radiation to eliminate the tumor. I just went numb.

My son was amazing. He remained focused and rose to the occasion. I couldn't think, ask any questions, even arrange for the schedule I needed to have in order to get the radiation going. Jonathan asked the necessary questions regarding having radiation. He also assisted me in scheduling the appointments that would be manageable and convenient for I would be going for radiation at City of Hope. This meant I'd be making the 3-hour round trip drive daily for 21 days straight and would need drivers if Fred was attending to his law practice.

Again, out of a difficult experience came a life long lesson. The unity one feels when faced with similar challenges, no matter what race, culture or religion you are makes such a difference.

For three weeks when I went to radiation, I formed relationships in the "Waiting Room" (you meet the same people who share your time slot repeatedly). I befriended a young Hispanic man who had just been released from prison, his mother, and an older gentleman who was a Holocaust survivor, who came with his two adult daughters. We had interesting daily conversations. I learned that no matter who you are, where you live, what you have in your bank account, as Cancer Fighters, we are forever connected. We formed our own support network during those weeks. I remember I was the first one done with receiving radiation. I gave them each a parting gift, The Giving Tree by Shel Silverstein, for they had taught me so much.

I was exhausted after I received all the radiation. But no matter what, I wanted to have the Thanksgiving Feast at my home this year.

My caretaker Tess, from the Philippines, honored my wishes, and NEVER having made a Thanksgiving feast before set out to learn. I told her to follow my directions, which I had to shout from the couch, for my fatigue was so difficult to manage that day I couldn't sit up.

Needless to say, what I thought would be so easy turned into a fiasco. Poor Tess was frazzled by making a meal that was totally unfamiliar to her (she made the most perfect rice in the world. I could never make that dish as well as she could. I should have served rice for that Thanksgiving). I was further depressed for I had lost control, and it didn't turn out the way I would have done it.

The bottom line was that nothing really mattered regarding the food. I looked around the table with my family sitting around me, and felt a sense of gratitude that was indescribable.

I now look back at that experience as one of my favorite Thanksgivings ever for I understood that holiday in a totally different dimension.

Although time may have felt like it stood still for me, the minutes did turn into hours, the hours did become whole days, and slowly but surely I was adapting to re-entering into the earth's atmosphere.

The winter holiday time was easier for me to adjust to; I felt more comfortable in my home. My strength was slowly returning. Tess decided that it was time I stand on my own two feet which did feel wonderful. I was surrounded again with my loved ones, feeling safe and secure.

EXPECT THE UNEXPECTED! WHAT GOES UP DOES COME DOWN...I WAS RIDING ON AN EMOTIONAL ROLLER COASTER.

After the holidays, when all my family returned to their homes, and my husband and my friends went back to work, the loneliness I felt was overwhelming.

I began to experience severe anxiety attacks. Out of nowhere, my heart would start beating rapidly, I'd start to sweat, my hands started shaking, and I became short of breath. I never knew when these attacks would start. It usually happened when I felt fearful, and insecure; as if I was going to be attacked by an unknown enemy. I addressed this issue with my oncologists, and was referred to a psychiatrist. The diagnosis was that I was suffering from a condition called Post Traumatic Syndrome Disorder; something I still struggle with today. However, after having the necessary medication along with the right therapy, I have learned to manage my PTSD.

Three months had passed since my transplant. I continued to see Dr. Vandermoelen at Hoag Hospital. I also went to City of Hope for additional tests and scans. I was having bone marrow taps every 6 months (I agreed to this when I signed on to be in the Zevalin Study for 5 years). The results showed that one of my side effects of the transplant was Myelodysplasia, a precondition to Leukemia.

I had to maintain the upkeep of my porto-catheter, or as I so lovingly called it, my "third breast" (you have to flush the porto-catheter lines with fluids and Heparin so it doesn't clot and can be used continuously for IV fluids - I had started to received infusions of Gamma-globulin about every 10 weeks for my immune system did not kick in - to this day I still have to received IVIGs about every 12 weeks, and suffer from some nasty side effects - that drug doesn't like me).

My return to a "normal life" was not turning out to be what I had envisioned. By springtime, I was more determined than ever to go back to my passion, my profession, return to teaching despite not being in the classroom for almost three years.

I still wanted to return to being the person I had been, the person I thought I knew. Little did I know or understand, that parallel to my body receiving healthy cells, my brain cells seemed to have been rearranged.

TRAVEL GUIDE TIPS

• *Demonstrating Gratitude: Expressing your gratitude to those that have helped you in so many different ways is so important. The intrinsic worth of a thank you note is priceless. Those special Doctors, Nurses, Nurses Aids, Technicians love receiving expressive notes as to how they made a difference in your life.*

• *LIMIT YOUR EXPECTATIONS ON YOUR RETURN HOME. You have been through a life altering event. Give yourself time to process what has happened to you. It is so hard to understand that while you were away, life did go on as usual. Outside changes did happen that you were not aware of...starting over is never easy.*

• *REMEMBER TO WEAR YOUR EXPLORER'S HAT! Make your return a new adventure. It is all part of your JOURNEY.*

CHAPTER 16

EMBRACING THE NEW ME

"The secret of health for both mind and body is not to mourn for the past, worry about the future, or anticipate troubles but to live in the present moment wisely and earnestly."

Buddha

Springtime...a time for new beginnings including starting the process of returning to the classroom. I couldn't contain my excitement! I was really going to be a teacher again. I would be spending my days doing what I loved to do, instead of being immersed in going for blood checks and treatments.

Though I was aware of the fact that changes had taken place at school during my absence, I thought I was just going to "get back on the horse," my prior knowledge from being a teacher for so many years would help accommodate my transition.

Prior to my medical leave, I had a shared contract with a "teacher's teacher." I first met this young lady during her job interview. She was right out of completing the Teaching Credential Program at UCI, and she was exceptional. Unfortunately, due to my illness, I never had the opportunity to work side by side with her, delivering the wonderful program to our students we had envisioned. Despite my unexpected and lengthy detour from teaching, this amazing teacher, who generously covered for me during my illness and absence, was still willing to share a job contract with me. We agreed to do a four/one split. She would work one day a week (Friday) and I would work from Monday to Thursday.

I thought I had a good sense of my energy level, and would be able to pace myself going back to work. I would lead a more balanced life, instead of living in the classroom for up to twelve hours a day, I would come home at a reasonable hour, and still have time for exercising, napping or other extra curricular activities.

WRONG! Returning to the world I left was the most challenging thing I had ever done. As hard as it was leaving the classroom, working as a Primary Educator who also does full inclusion (mainstreaming Special Needs students) was so much more difficult.

I TRULY WAS NOT PREPARED!

Life had gone on without me. There were years of new procedures, new curriculums, new State Standards to learn. There was also a new requirement, getting a mandatory CLAD license (Cross-cultural, Language, and Academic Development) which ensured that all credentialed teachers were culturally sensitive, and used appropriate teaching techniques when teaching children who had English as their second language.

In order to get this supplemental credential I had to be licensed prior to entering back into the classroom. The only way this could be done was by taking a CRASH course; coursework everyday from 8:00 a.m. - 4:00 p.m. for three straight weeks, with the 6 hour exam immediately after.

During my school career I was plagued by test anxiety. I hated racing against the time clock in a test environment. This anxiety was now coupled with new obstacles; I had difficulty processing language quickly (I read and understood printed material at a much slower pace after having all the chemotherapy drugs) and retrieving information was a struggle despite all the preparations I had taken.

The class and scheduled test I was to take was in August of 2005. I was to return to teaching that September, almost a year after my bone marrow transplant.

Besides having the pressure to study for this required credential, Fred was determined to also continue with a project we had talked about prior to my illness, the remodeling of our kitchen.

Based on his opinion and view point, doing a kitchen was "no big deal." He was right...it was not a "big deal" it was an ENORMOUS DEAL.

I was feeling fragmented and stressed by my return to my professional world, and I had lost the confidence I once had as a teacher, for what I thought would be familiar to me was foreign to me. Even meeting with the grade level staff in a planning session prior to my starting class brought me to tears. I understood medical language better than I understood educational words.

DEMOLITION OF OUR KITCHEN STARTED EXACTLY ON THE FIRST DAY OF MY NEW CREDENTIAL PROGRAM.

I could relate to that action word. I felt demolished both physically and emotionally. I'd had a bone marrow tap the week before to check on my medical condition. I felt sore in my buttocks area (that pain can last up to two weeks), and sitting on a chair for eight hours a day didn't help. Even using a pillow didn't help much.

On top of feeling overwhelmed and confused by all that was happening in my life, I had a moment of weakness regarding getting another cat. My beloved cat of eighteen years, a red Persian named CJ (Cory Junior) had died in December. Fred and I only wanted to have a red Persian to replace CJ (not a good idea, you can never replace a beloved animal, all animals are different despite having similar features).

Ironically, during the second day of my class, while I was reading the want ads during my lunch break, I spotted an advertisement for a red Persian kitten.

Without too much thought, right after class, I drove to the town with the necessary cash in my wallet, to get our brand new kitten. What could go wrong, did go wrong. I got lost for two hours, I needed to find a bathroom ASAP for I have a "nervous stomach," and I walked into the home of the owners of the kitten, only to be shocked at their living conditions.

The owners had cages and litter boxes everywhere. There were all sorts of dogs and cats. Since having all the chemotherapy I had, I am more sensitive to smells: and the smell in that house nearly knocked me out.

Despite all these obstacles, I found what I was looking for. In the corner of the living room where I was standing, there was a tiny red Persian cat, looking fearful and shivering. Within two minutes, I had this kitten in my hands, paid the necessary money to purchase it, and ran out.

Here I was two days into resuming what I thought would be a "Normal Life," feeling totally out of touch with my surroundings. My kitchen was a disaster, I was overloaded with my test preparations, and I had just adopted a kitten. As the kitten and I looked at each other, I remembered the words my husband used in difficult times "Power Forward."

Fred is an avid fan of the Lakers. When the Lakers are playing basketball, there are certain house rules we have to abide by, like for nothing short of an emergency could Fred's game watching be interrupted. (Even when I was losing my hair, if the Laker game was on it was questionable whether I could go to Fred for support. I did. I came out of the bathroom, with a huge bundle of hair in each hand. Fred's response to me was, "You think you got problems, the Lakers are down by 15." I started hysterically laughing at the absurdity of the situation. Yes, Fred was kidding...but it still is always about the Lakers!)

Power forward. I named the new red Persian kitten Lily Laker. I even bought her a purple collar and attached a yellow ribbon to it.

Having a new kitten to train, cooking over a camp stove in the living room, going to class and studying for the exam, all made me want to crawl under my covers and hide. I certainly did not expect any of these emotions!

Time moved quickly, before I knew it I was standing in front of my classroom, the very classroom I had been in three years before when I received the phone call telling me that I had cancer. It all felt surreal to me, I was a stranger in a strange land.

Three years ago, I'd left that room within 24 hours of the phone call from the doctor, with no time to put my belongings away. In my absence, it had been used by other teachers. Coming back into the same classroom, looking for my supplies, books and materials was eerie. I had no recollection of where anything was.

Aside from not finding my old materials, I had to get familiar with the brand new set of instructional manuals, trade and text books the first grade students were using. I had no clue how to put the program together despite all the generous help my grade level staff gave me. Luckily, I had my "Angel," my teaching partner who had experienced this curriculum, to help me. She walked me through what I needed to do.

Each minute I was in the room setting up, I was getting more and more anxious. I didn't think I could remember how to teach. I was TERRIFIED. My own husband didn't understand, all he remembered was the woman he knew before the transplant, how confident and strong I was, never backing down from any teaching challenge. He really didn't know what to do with me, especially since all I talked about was returning to teach.

There was a staff meeting set up just before we had to start our school year. I remember sitting amongst the teachers, who were once so familiar to me, but now seemed so foreign. The principal, whom I really respected and appreciated for all the support she gave me, started to run the meeting.

She opened with what I thought was a joke. I thought she was trying to put us all at ease for all teachers' nerves are shaken just before they open their doors to new students.

The principal began by saying "It's all about nuts. The nuts are to be in this area and the non nuts are to be in the opposite area."

I started hysterically laughing, thinking wow...how daring she is to address students as "nuts" or "nutty." I know that teachers can think what they want about students but to say that word out loud!

The more she talked about nuts the more hysterical I got. I was laughing alone. The principal was talking about handling students with nut allergies. The staff was just staring at me, probably thinking that I had been rendered "nuts" as a result of all I had been through.

My first reintroduction to the staff was so embarrassing. The other focus that I was unfamiliar with was "it's all about testing results."

Here I was so happy I no longer had to focus on testing results, for in my case, if I had poor testing results, I would possibly need more chemotherapy or radiation. Yet, all I heard was the discussion of "test results" and how we had to raise the children's reading and math scores.

At the conclusion of the staff meeting, we all ran back to our classrooms to finish setting up and reviewing the students we were going to have for the year (knowing there would be many changes in the beginning of the school year).

My partner and I reviewed our new students. We realized we had a large number of those with specialized needs, and no additional assistance. We even had a student who didn't speak one word of English. By the end of the day, the day before school was to start, I was a wreck. I didn't know how I was ever going to get through the first day of school, let alone the school year.

The one thing I did know was that I was not in a hospital, not hooked up to any IVs, not wearing a hospital gown or pajamas, and I was not worrying about the results of all the medical tests I was taking.

Looking at what I did have, MY DREAM OF TEACHING COMING TRUE, I started to breathe a little more easily.

THE FIRST DAY OF SCHOOL AFTER A THREE YEAR ABSENCE...IN THE VERY SAME CLASSROOM I TAUGHT!

Traditionally, the first day of school, a most exciting day for both children and parents, the families line up in front of their assigned classrooms. Every year, I disguised myself, wearing a silly hat, glasses and always carrying a camera, and stood behind the parents, waiting along with them to meet "Mrs. Pardes."

This year, I continued with my tradition. I found a hat that had two rims with the inscription reading "Which Way Did My Leader Go?"...a perfect hat for there were going to be two teachers in this classroom. I knew that many students were new to the school, or they were too young to remember a Mrs. Pardes. Somehow, I was able to stand in line with the new students, and parents, asking those standing next to me, "Have you ever heard of Mrs. Pardes?" or I would say, "I heard Mrs. Pardes is the meanest teacher in the whole school!"

I was finally able to relax, smile, laugh and marvel at how far I had come. My friend's daughter who was starting her own Student Teaching Program wanted to observe how I opened a class the first day of school. Seeing her face with a smile on it also made me feel that I was in control and I would be just fine.

JUST FINE...that feeling only lasted for a few moments.

After going to the front of the line, introducing myself as Mrs. Pardes, and introducing my partner, I looked around at those beautiful first grade faces. My eyes stopped on a most darling little girl, her smile was radiant, her eyes actually twinkled with excitement. Then I saw what she was holding.

A BOOK ENTITLED, "FACTS CHILDREN SHOULD KNOW ABOUT LEUKEMIA."

Within that one second, I found myself startled at a word that always made me uncomfortable, fearful.

As she walked into the classroom, she handed me the book asking that I read it to the class today. She also introduced me to her teenaged sister who was stunningly sporting a hair-do that I knew very well, "The Bald Look." The student proceeded to tell me that her older sister had leukemia and was receiving chemotherapy.

We wear many hats as a teacher, one of which is the hat of an "Actor." My heart melted for the girl who had Leukemia, and I felt for the entire family. But the only emotion I showed was a smile on my face, never revealing how I was feeling, a feeling of empathy and understanding for I walked in the same shoes. I felt so lucky that I would be able to help the student have a better understanding of the medical and emotional processes you go through when facing this illness.

The students and their families loved seeing the classroom all set up, with a sentiment of excitement for all the new things these first graders were going to learn.

After the parents left, I was hit with a sudden wave of exhaustion. I actually had "jelly legs." I still don't know how I got through the very first day.

Looking at the enlarged photo in my home office of me standing amongst the students , with my Angel partner standing by the doorway, I still am awed at the fact that MIRACLES DO COME TRUE. THE IMPOSSI-BLE IS POSSIBLE.   MRS. PARDES HONORED HER PROMISE TO HER STUDENTS AND CAME BACK!

TRAVEL GUIDE TIPS

• *Try to understand that learning is a process. Keep a Daily Learning Journal, noting what educational challenges you faced today, and what knowledge you gained from those experiences.*

• *Identify the things you are having difficulties with. Then take each item, and break it down into smaller pieces to make it more manageable.*

• *Don't get stuck in "quicksand." Sometimes it is best when you reach your level of frustration just to "stop." Distract yourself with something that makes you feel peaceful.*

• *Go backwards in order to go forward. Get in touch with your beginnings to get to where you need to be today.*

• *Keep it simple. Don't try to do too much. Remember your "today's abilities". You are going to adjust physically and mentally to your new / old surroundings, it just is going to take time. Nothing stays the same, change is constant.*

CHAPTER 17

LOST AND FOUND

"Keep your dreams alive. Understand to achieve anything requires faith and belief in yourself, vision, hard work, determination, and dedication. Remember all things are possible for those who believe."

Gail Devers

I had already learned that you can never go home again, nothing ever stays the same. What once was natural to me, standing in front of a classroom, teaching, had become foreign and unfamiliar. I may have looked like the same teacher that left three years earlier, but I certainly was not the same person.

NO PAIN, NO GAIN.

Going back, having to relearn skills that once were so natural and easy for me, was so hard! I felt like an impostor who didn't belong to the teaching profession. I felt like I didn't know what I was doing, how were the children ever going to learn to read and write from me? I was not the experienced teacher that I thought I was, I was a "Virgin Teacher," learning how to deliver lessons as if it were the very first time.

I WAS HUMBLED!

I had always been the one to lend a helping hand to other teachers. I had been a mentor teacher, I taught student teachers how to teach. And now I was the student teacher, learning from those that once were my peers.

Admitting you need help, as easy as it sounds, is one of the most difficult things you have to do. I had to learn to ask for help. And I did!

Starting over again, working with technical programs that I had never used, also contributed to my anxiety level.

The old fashioned report cards, where you hand write the grades and teacher comments, had become obsolete. I now had to do report cards electronically, on line.

The very first inservice where the instructor had to explain how to input data and print the report cards, was way above my head. My lack of understanding of what was being presented triggered a major anxiety attack. I started to sweat profusely, turning bright red. Those physical characteristics of my attack were very hard to hide. I felt everyone staring at me. The feeling was awful.

Yet, despite how horrible I felt, I got through it. I learned that although people nod in agreement during presentations as if they understand everything the first time they hear it, is not necessarily true. People fear raising their hands, fear asking questions, or asking for help. No one wants to look stupid.

There was no way for me to get through my days as a "New/Old" teacher without asking questions. I needed help, and I began to not be afraid to ask for it.

Fortunately, having my Angel partner's support, love and extreme patience made this process of re-entry so much easier and smoother.

Before I knew it, despite all the obstacles I faced, including physiological challenges (I tired easily and had GI problems), I had taught 180 days straight. I didn't take off one sick day. I felt victorious that I had overcome my feelings of being inept. I found my new center, and with the combination of my old skills and newly developed ones, I was once again confident enough to call myself a "TEACHER."

WITH EACH SUNRISE, COMES SUNSET...

THEN BLACK CLOUDS HOVERED OVER MY HEAD...

I entered my second year as a primary teacher with the same hope and belief that I would make a difference in children's lives. However, as much as I wanted to continue in the profession, my body did not want to follow my desire.

Going to work daily became a bigger struggle for me, physiologically. Just getting up in the morning, getting dressed, and eating breakfast in a designated amount of time was difficult because of my bathroom issues. I used to pray that I could make it all the way to school without having to stop and look for a restroom. Reflecting back, I still don't know how I survived physically and emotionally. This issue was my own personal secret for I was embarrassed to discuss it with my husband, family or friends. I was traumatized from having "accidents" in the hospital for not being able to control my bodily functions.

One of the other side effects from having the bone marrow transplant was having a compromised immune system. Being under the stressful situation I was in while I was teaching created even more havoc with my low antibody counts. I was catching colds continuously, and I battled with bouts of pneumonia. In general, I was taking a beating.

My darling protective husband, along with my mother, sister and brother-in-law realized how challenged I was and spoke up. They felt that I had survived against all odds, and now I was putting my health in jeopardy.

My health should have been my priority. It wasn't.

I refused to listen to the voice of reason for I NEVER WANTED TO BE HOME ALONE AGAIN, FEELING THAT HORRIBLE SENSE OF ISOLATION.

There comes a time, when no matter how hard you fight, or how badly you want things to be different, you have to accept what is. I began to understand that risking my life was not an appropriate choice.

I CHOSE LIFE AND TURNED IN MY RESIGNATION PAPERS IN APRIL. I would complete the school year, then retire from teaching in June.

When one door closes, another one does open. My daughter and her husband were going to have a baby in May. I was going to be a grandmother and hold my very first grandchild, something I'd feared I might never live to do.

Mentally, I started envisioning myself having a life without teaching in the classroom. I also started daydreaming how wonderful it would be to be part of a new life, and watch my grandson grow.

My grandson was born in May. June was right around the corner. Upon my return from visiting my children and new born grandson, I started to pack my classroom.

That act alone brought the reality that this time I was leaving for good. There would be no going back to the classroom. My career was over.

I was devastated. I cried in the car everyday I went to work. I tried holding on to every special moment I had with the children in the classroom.

The day had come...the end of my career was here...it was time to say good-bye.

The graduation ceremony that I did every year using the theme and book "Oh, The Places You'll Go" by Dr. Seuss was heavily attended by my students and their families. This year I ran the ceremony with such a heavy heart. The chapter of Mrs. Pardes Teaching had ended.

I left that day a broken person. My family and friends were so delighted for me. They all felt I SHOULD BE SO HAPPY. I certainly didn't feel that way.

In honor of my retirement, Fred planned a trip to see The Wimbledon Tennis Tournament in London. We were also to go on a tour throughout Spain. He wanted to make me so happy and thought that traveling would be the answer.

The trip that was to be filled with celebrating my retirement, turned out to be a fiasco. Everything that could go wrong did. From sitting in the middle seat in the airplane, and having Fred accidently spill beer on my lap, to getting sick on the plane from the smell of the beer, and arriving in London totally depleted.

There is no joy in traveling when one is not feeling well. My focus was not on the tennis games, but on finding restrooms. I had just had an infusion of Gamma-globulin with a larger than normal amount of Predni-sone. Not only was I not feeling well, my emotions were totally out of whack as a result of this steroid.

Due to the policy in Wimbeldon, when there is a switch on the court, you are not allowed to return to your seats. I had to use the restroom repeatedly, leaving Fred constantly wondering where I was, with no way of finding out. He firmly was against bringing a cell phone for he wanted to feel like he was on vacation, and not be bothered with having the possibility of anyone calling him.

What he didn't anticipate was the necessity of having cell phones in unfamiliar environments, especially traveling with a sick wife, having side effects due to the drugs she took.

My husband is a problem solver. He was unable to purchase a cell phone in London due to some security reason, so when we arrived in Spain, he purchased "Walkie Talkies." I think we were probably the only two people using that tool to communicate and even that wasn't fool proof.

Walkie Talkies are only good when each of you has one. Fred, busily showing one of our traveling companions the two walkie talkies he purchased, was not paying attention to where I was walking. He thought he was following me, someone short with dark hair, wearing a blue dress (he is not too strong in the tiny detail department). That person turned out to be a stranger.   I was left in a small piazza in Granada, Spain, alone, with no means of communication or finding my husband.

Needless to say I was fuming. I remember sitting in some small alleyway, next to a very good singer and guitar player, with a hat filled with money in front of him. I started thinking if Fred doesn't show up, I too could do the same (small problem...I didn't have a hat, nor the voice to warrant anyone giving me money). By some sheer miracle my husband found me sitting next to the singer.   My singing career ended in less than an hour.

The trip continued to have many more challenging moments including being stuck in an un-air conditioned pension in Blois.   They were having a heat wave...the temperature was over 110 degrees.

I only wanted to go home, be in my own bed, and feel safe. I didn't even think about my retirement. The trip finally ended, we returned home. Little did I know that I was going to enter a very dark period, one where I had no direction, no longer knew who I was, or what I wanted to be when I grew up.

The first September of my retirement I was filled with total emptiness. School had started, and I was not in the classroom. To make matters worse, every time I took a walk I would hear the sounds of children playing from a school adjacent to my home. Sounds that I loved hearing when I was actively teaching became so painful to me. I had a sentimental attachment to that school. It was where I had started my career as a school teacher and had built so many wonderful memories. Walking by the school was a constant reminder of what I had lost.

Eventually, and slowly, I started making some progress towards my own recovery. I sought professional help. My therapist was one who knew me so well for she had "walked by my side" as the therapist when I was engaged in a cancer support group.

I mourned the loss of my former self, but began to understand that I needed to connect who I was before to who I had become and where I wanted to go. I always said that life is about Legos. Everything is interconnected.

My passion has always been storytelling, and I loved to teach. I came up with an idea that I would start a curriculum using children's literature as a catalyst for thematic and meaningful discussions. I entitled that course "Children's Stories for the Eyes of the Wise." I had the privilege of delivering these well received presentations at a retirement facility.

I also started to redefine what I thought teaching was for me at that moment. I realized I never stopped being a teacher, the only thing that changed was the environment I was teaching in. The world became my classroom.

Wherever I went, I found people who had struggled with similar challenges I had battling cancer. I started coaching people, and providing them insight for the fight of their lives. I also started doing public speaking engagements on a variety of topics including cancer.

Before I knew it, I was "back in the saddle," my life was full and had meaning. I happily found my new identity, I am now known as ...

Michelle Pardes, Still Breathing, A Survivorship Coach.

FAREWELL FROM YOUR TRAVEL GUIDE

You are engaged in a most difficult journey, riding on an emotional roller coaster where changes occur by the minute. I have provided you with tips that have been successful for me. Please know that part of your journey is your own discovery of what works for you. I look forward to hearing from you and learning about your own amazing success stories. Remember to become another traveler's guide who is embarking on a similar trip. Pay forward the lessons you have learned so others too can feel encouraged and reassured that they will successfully navigate their own journeys.

I would like to dedicate the following poem to my fellow travelers. Listen to the words carefully, understand the value of your true worth, remember where there is life, there is always hope. REMEMBER TO STOP, BREATHE, AND ENJOY THE VIEW OF THIS BEAUTIFUL WORLD.

Share your successes with the world.

Inspire others to reach for their own stars.

Let your achievements stand as a shining example that goals can be attained, fears can be conquered, and dreams really can come true when we have the courage to pursue them.

Jason Blume

ABCs to help you reach your destination

Pack the following ABC words and their messages for assistance on your journey of twists, turns and unexpected challenges.

PPROACH:

So many people will be approaching you on your journey. You will be greeted by family, friends, your community all with good intentions to help you travel on a path you never selected. You feel overwhelmed, anxious, confused, and exhausted for you lack the energy to talk.

REMEMBER:

As confused as you are being a new voyager, so are the people that you encounter. Try to find your own personal responses that put you and the person who is speaking to you at ease. You have control over the length of your conversation. Be aware of your own comfort level and energy level. If you just want an "in and out" conversation find a compact response that communicates gratitude for their concern, yet be firm that you do not want to go into details over personal issues you are facing on your journey. When asked "how are you" I found that using "still breathing" works beautifully, allowing those that are partaking in the conversation the ability to relate to that simple response that says so much.

"Birds sing after a storm. Why shouldn't we?"

Rose Fitzgerald Kennedy

ELIEVE:

When your symptoms begin to appear, you first can't believe what you are feeling or seeing. You begin to convince yourself that your imagination is on overdrive. The next step can come in the form of you becoming a "river rafter", selecting the perfect river to ride on; The River of Denial. As time progresses, along with symptoms that don't disappear, you begin to feel anxious, sometimes wearing the hat of a physician doing research and then diagnosing yourself with a life threatening illness.

REMEMBER:

What you are seeing and feeling are signs that things are not typical and appropriate with your body. Honesty is the best policy. The sooner you go to the appropriate professionals that can help discover what is wrong, the sooner the right intervention can be found. As hard as it is to hear the truth, initially feeling like you want to "flight," you will adapt, and "fight" for your life!

"In the middle of every difficulty
lies opportunity"

Albert Einstein

*C*HANGES:

From your birth to where you are today, you are always in a "State of Change". Physiologically we grow and mature; Emotionally you have implemented a variety of coping mechanisms to help you manage life's challenges. However, NO ONE CAN PREPARE THEMSELVES FOR LIFE ALTERING EVENTS.

REMEMBER:

Once you learn the truth of your illness; you need to give yourself consent to feel what you feel, process the information in the time that you need, cry, scream, holler if you have to. Then, you need to remember to try to adopt an "I can do it" attitude. There is nothing better than having the book "The Little Engine That Could" displayed in a visible area. Begin each day with the mantra "I think I can, I think I can, I think I can" face my challenges for today. Having that "can do it positive attitude" helps you face so many difficult challenges. It also helps those that are working with you to equally feel the positive energy, something that is much needed during those trying moments.

"Life's challenges are not supposed to paralyze you, they're supposed to help you discover who you are"

Bernice Johnson Reagan

Directions:

No matter how carefully you follow all the directions, do what is necessary to do, take the necessary treatment, one can still get lost and confused.

REMEMBER:

Even when you are experiencing the feeling of being "lost alone in a dark forest", you will find your way. You will face the unexpected. You will take detours, things won't go the way you expected, you will need to find your own center, your own way out towards healing. Be creative, compromise and be flexible. There will be things that you do that might not be successful. Pick yourself up, and arm yourself with hope. Perhaps the next time you will find the solution to your problem. You can learn more from losing than winning. No pain..No gain. One has to take risks in order to get rewards.

"Yesterday I dared to struggle, today I dared to win"

Bernadette Devlin

ENERGY:

When you face a life altering event, you feel depleted, overwhelmed, thinking and walking become an effort. You feel you lack energy to do anything constructive, sitting and staring seems all you can muster. Combine that with necessary medical interventions, and you are at a "Stand Still"...no bodily movement is taking place.

REMEMBER:

Even though you are feeling physiologically and emotionally depleted, force yourself to get up. Put one foot in front of the other, go for a walk outside, exercise will help you energize. Mental exercise is equally as necessary. Reading a long novel might require too much energy, however magazines, newspapers, any light reading will help you stimulate your brain. Sometimes you'll have an overactive brain, where all you can think about is your predicament. That is mentally exhausting! Engage in mentally enlightening exercises that hold your interest.

"If you don't row your canoe, you can't move"

Katharine Hepburn

FAITH:

No matter what religion you are, the one thing that is most necessary is having faith. Prayer can bring you hope, and strength. My father-in-law who fought in the first wave on D Day quoted a familiar statement based on his own experience, "there is no such thing as an atheist in a fox hole".

REMEMBER:

Do what it takes to help you feel strong. It is a known fact that prayer can give you courage to face so many difficult challenges you are facing. Don't be afraid to ask someone to pray for you. Also ask to be blessed prior to going through the multitude of medical challenges and tests that you face during your illness.

The word "blessing" is connected to the word blood in English. Brother David states that a blessing is like the spiritual bloodstream that flows through the universe. Being blessed is also like the blood coming from the heart and going back to the heart.

"People living deeply have no fear of death"

Anais Nin

GOALS:

So many changes take place when you "Enter the Land of the Unexpected". After feeling divorced from what was once familiar to you, you begin to get your "walking legs" on. Setting specific goals either daily, weekly, monthly or annually help you look forward to a desired accomplishment, helping empower you to achieve significant milestones, therefore making you feel successful.

REMEMBER:

Life does go on after your diagnosis. It many not look familiar to you, yet once you begin to adapt, you can persevere, reach new heights, and find satisfaction in embarking on new meaningful adventures.

"Obstacles are those things you see when you take your eyes off the goal"

Hannah More

Health:

In order to return to "good" health there are many different "rules and regulations" you need to adhere to and follow. You need to take a holistic approach and remember the body and mind connection.

REMEMBER:

There are six letters in the word HEALTH. H stands for hard work. Roll up your sleeves, and put on your "I can do it" attitude. E stands for eating. Stick to a healthy eating plan incorporating fruits, vegetables, and protein. Drink six to eight glasses of water a day. A glass of red wine at night is good for your heart and your mood. A stands for attitude. It is extremely difficult being ill, and dealing with the side effects of medications. Keep a "Thank You" list, write three daily items as a reminder of what we have, instead of what we don't have. L is for listen. We learn so much if we listen to what others have to say. T stands for try. Give it all you have. Make a valid effort at things that seem impossible for you. Effort is half the battle. H stands for happy. At the end of each day in my classroom I used to wish my students to have a H-A-P-P-Y D-A-Y. THAT IS WHAT I WISH FOR YOU EACH DAY.

"Make your own recovery the first priority in your life"

Robin Norwood

INSIGHT:

After being given your diagnosis is, you can not find your bearings, or imagine yourself getting to the next second. You are frozen in terror, hoping and feeling that what you are experiencing is not reality; that you are asleep experiencing a nightmare. Once you gain some clarity, you begin to have new insights, seeing what was once so ordinary, become so special.

REMEMBER:

Going through this life altering experience brings you insights that you have never experienced before. Your relationships with those you love carry a different meaning, your vision of life changes. Seeing your natural surroundings, the sun, flowers, trees become brilliant. Moments when you are outside versus being in a hospital or in isolation at home, are to be treasured. Living takes on a whole new meaning!

"Vision without action is a dream. Action without vision is simply passing the time. Action with vision is make a positive difference."

Joel Barker

JOB:

You have entered a world where the number one job is to help you return to health. You become the "receiver" of health services, instead of the "provider" of your usual job duties. Your daily routine, professional, and social world, disappears. Your new profession is to learn new skills, vocabulary, priorities and systems; all related to your disease and recovery. You are a full-time patient.

REMEMBER:

You now have a new job title: "Patient". With it comes many demands: paper work, schedules, and side effects to manage. You must also gain knowledge to be able to act as your own health advocate. You can become inundated with paper work, appointments, consultations, and making choices you are unfamiliar with. This job is difficult to manage - you need to ask for help. Find "personnel" to delegate responsibilities to. "Hire" family and friends you trust to be a secretary for paperwork, a reporter for visiting doctors, an assistant to help you make decisions, and a home helper. No man is an island. It requires a team to help you be successful!

"We are drowning in information -
but starved for knowledge"

John Naisbitt

Kick:

There will be days you'll feel you can not handle another doctor visit, more bad news, another blood test, scan, or x-ray. There will be days when you are hospitalized when all you want is sleep, but you are constantly prodded, checked, or weighed, day and night. There will be times medical professionals don't think before they speak, or casually drop information that is difficult to process (i.e. your chemotherapy was not successful, your cancer is still present, you need to start a new therapeutic intervention tomorrow). You'll want to holler, scream, and kick someone.

REMEMBER:

Being human means we experience a full range of emotions, from excitement and happiness to terror and fear (especially when it comes to illnesses). It is acceptable to be angry. It is also perfectly reasonable to ask for the treatment you desire. Anyone involved in giving care should know to respect those that they are dealing with, including their families. This means demonstrating empathy, using less frightening words, and providing a forum for asking questions.

"Perhaps our eyes need to be washed by our tears once in a while, so that we can see Life with clearer view again."

Alex Tan

181

LABELS:

"Hello, my name is ___ I am short, with brown hair and brown eyes. I like to eat hot dogs, play tennis, and read." I AM A PERSON. Once you receive your diagnosis, you begin to lose your identity. You are ___, who has ___. You are labeled, placed in a category, part of a club you never chose to join.

REMEMBER:

You are not a label. Your diagnosis, your illness, does not replace you as a person. It does not define you. It is just something you are going through. Educate others that you are still you, no matter what. Many people you encounter are equally terrified of having this illness visit them. Communicate that, you are still the same person you were before, yet have added a new dimension because of your present experience. We learn from our experiences. By looking at our situations, listening to those we are involved with, we are learning so many things about ourselves and others. Embrace who you have become, which is definitely not a label, but an individual who is a survivor.

"Labels are for filing. Labels are for clothing. Labels are NOT for people."

Martina Navratilova

Mentor:

Wearing "new shoes" on your journey can give you the "wobbly effect". You trying to orient yourself, to become familiar with new paths you need to take. Steady yourself with a variety of support systems including a mentor. That individual can be someone you are comfortable with and trust, who has insights or experience in what you are going through. Revealing your emotions to those that are close to you can be difficult, especially if you do not want to worry them. But, you need to have the appropriate guidance to help you get through this difficult time.

REMEMBER:

We have many innovative programs, and facilities that provide us with professionals who can give us a helping hand in managing our emotions, fears and anxieties. You have the freedom to speak your mind without burdening those you love who are equally battling with their own fears and anxieties. Having the appropriate leader/coach can make a huge difference in assisting us on this journey.

"Trusting our intuition often saves us from disaster"

Anne Wilson Schaef

NORMAL:

"When are things going to get back to normal?" This is a question that is perpetually asked by the traveler and those that are involved with him/her. We have so many experiences from childhood to adulthood that impact us and who we become. Normal is momentary, connected with your present. As you progress through life's path, you experience many things that are difficult. We all want to go back to the days when all was peaceful, uncomplicated and NORMAL.

REMEMBER:

You are now entering a new normal. Because of this experience; changes that take place, medications that produce side effects, the ripple effect of trauma (sometimes defined as post traumatic syndrome disorder), you can never go backwards, only forward. Don't be afraid of the new normal. You will adapt, and adjust. It will take time. Be kind and patient to yourself. In the future, you will suddenly realize that what was once unfamiliar has become part of who you have become.

"Normal fear protects us; abnormal fear paralyses us. Normal fear motivates us to improve our individual and collective welfare; abnormal fear constantly poisons and distorts our inner lives. Our problem is not to be rid of fear but, rather to harness and master it."

Martin Luther King, JR.

*O*PTIONS:

Making choices that affect our futures starts for most of us at around age 18. As adults, choice is part of life. But when you have a life threatening illness, your choices can mean life or death. You feel over-whelmed, totally lost as to what is best for you. You ask for facts, you are presented with percentages, no one knows with certainty what the outcome will be. While you might be insecure in making decisions, you want to have choices. You want to have OPTIONS!

REMEMBER:

Doctors know the most successful protocol to use with predictable cancers.. However, there are always new formations of cells, new mutations, new cancers. There-fore the need for up to date OPTIONS to use to help eradicate these cancers relies heavily on research. Hav-ing had a cancer that didn't respond to the typical inter-ventions, all I ever wanted to hear from my physicians was that I had another alternative, another option. I was always willing to take a risk to possibly give me the reward of a cancer free life. As long as you have OP-TIONS you have a chance. NEVER, NEVER GIVE UP!! Look, research, learn. KNOWLEDGE IS POWER!

"Nine Tenths of education is encouragement."

Anatele France

$\mathcal{P}$LEASE:

No matter how difficult the situation you are in, how low you are feeling, know that all who are involved with your care are trying hard to accommodate you. There will be times medical professionals are abrupt with you, yet that still doesn't mean we should "forget our manners". Being well mannered matters. Such simple words like "Please" and "Thank You" should be used by all involved. The same goes for the medical professionals. Showing respect to the patient and their families is of utmost importance. Setting that type of climate helps ease a stressful situation, and makes the patient feel important and significant.

REMEMBER:

Treating your fellow man, no matter who they are, with manners and respect makes a difference in how they behave. When one is treated with "honey" you get a much sweeter delivery of what is being asked of you. Emotions do run high in hospital settings, it is difficult for all involved, yet no matter what , we still have to remember: treat others as we wish to be treated.

"Manners are a sensitive awareness of the feelings of others. If you have that awareness, you have good manners, no matter what fork you use."

Emily Post

QUESTIONS:

We learn by asking questions. There is no such a thing as a stupid question. Unfortunately, doctors and other medical personnel have limited time to spend on each patient. You deserve to know why certain things are being done, what side effects you might experience, risks, and other variables that could happen as a result of the medical intervention being used.

REMEMBER:

To get the information you need to know, plan, as best you can, the questions that need to be asked of the doctor. Pre-write your questions. I also have sent off the questions via e-mail, which allowed the doctor to prepare prior to our consultation.

Questions regarding drugs and effects can most likely be answered. But some questions are quite difficult to answer. No doctor has a crystal ball. No one can see into our future.

Family members may have questions that might make the patient uncomfortable. Ask the patient to give the doctor permission to disclose their information and speak to the doctor privately.

"One who asks a question is a fool for five minutes, one who does not ask a question remains a fool forever."

Chinese proverb

READY:

No matter how prepared you think you are for hearing your diagnosis - having to "take off" into the Land of Hospitals and Doctors - you can't ever be ready for what you are about to partake in. You are also never ready to return to the Land of Normal when you are done with your chemotherapy/radiation or other medical procedure. Your experience is comparable to that of an Astronaut. You are blasted out into a different "Space," floating with all the medications they give you, then you have to adapt to "Earth's Atmosphere" upon re-entry. Getting to feel grounded again takes time. In a strange way, you are more comfortable living in "Space," protected by medical intervention, than when you are cut off from those "life lines."

REMEMBER:

When you are handed shocking news such as the diagnosis of cancer, you can't even imagine how you are going to feel or react. Every person reacts in ways that are beyond their control. Please do not feel embarrassed or apologetic for your response to this most difficult announcement.

"The world is round and the place which may seem like the end may also be the beginning"

Ivy Baker Priest

Sense of Humor:

Cancer isn't funny. Hospitals are not fun. You hurt, you're scared, you're lonely, even angry. While we've all heard that "laughter is the best medicine," it can feel as though you'll never laugh again.

REMEMBER:

Even when things appear the most bleak, when all you feel like doing is lying in bed under the covers, you can find something amusing and comical. There are times when you might look in the mirror and just start laughing at yourself. Please know the way you might see yourself now will not last forever.

Hospitals in Israel have found that there is a definite significant positive emotional effect from providing humor to their patients. One of the hospitals even hired a clown to attend daily to bring joy and funny moments to those that are in the hospital.

Surround yourself with upbeat people who will attempt to lighten things up. Renting funny movies, reading joke books or listening to comedians on TV or on DVDs can also bring you moments of laughter.

"A good laugh and a long sleep are the best cures in the doctor's book."

Irish proverb

THINK:

Your brain has many jobs. One of its most important jobs is giving us the ability to think. In times when all is well with your universe, your brain signals you and the rest of your body to feel "at ease".

When faced with life altering events such as a medical crisis, all you think about is your crisis. You wake up thinking about your situation, your conversations are about the problems you are facing, you go to sleep with this heavy baggage. Your brain is on overdrive, your body reacting to a steady stream of "What is going to happen to me? Will I ever be okay?"

REMEMBER:

You were invaded by the unexpected. Now a large part of your healing job is trying to keep balanced emotionally. You have to learn to live simultaneously with your illness, maintaining a self imposed restriction on "crisis thinking time." To accomplish this difficult task, find things that can preoccupy you and allow you to feel joy. Explore activities that can hold your interest. Getting your brain to shut off is hard work, but with perseverance you will get back to a good place.

"Love the moment. Flowers grow out of dark moments. Therefore, each moment is vital. It affects the whole. Life is a succession of such moments and to live each, is to succeed."

Corita Kent

190

UNDERSTANDING:

It takes a while for you to get to a place where you have some understanding of what is happening to you and your life as a result of your illness. Your life as you knew it no longer exists. Everything has changed. Your feelings can be quite confusing, you can be feeling a sense of "it is not fair this is happening to me", or feelings of rage and anger. Getting to the place of "acceptance" and understanding your new life is a process.

REMEMBER:

Adjusting to your new circumstances does not happen over night. There are many things one can actively do in order to get to a place where you can handle your challenge.

Seek counsel from mental health professionals. Finding a person you feel comfortable with might take time, but once you establish a relationship, you can experience great benefits. You can also receive huge benefits speaking with other people who are traveling in similar shoes. Supports groups offer empathy and reassurance along with a variety of resources (finding services, therapists, etc.).

"Life is like a mirror, we get the best results when we smile at it."

Unknown

Visitors:

Once the word is out about your illness, the kindness of family, friends and community is demonstrated in many loving ways. You receive phone calls, emails, flowers, cards, and delicious home cooked meals. Visitors come by to ask how you are doing.

It is a wonderful to see and be touched by all this love, yet it can get OVERWHELMING. Going through what you are going through can not only be physically depleting but emotionally exhausting.

REMEMBER:

Your well-wishers need to understand that peace and tranquility are great healers. Enlist a few close people to run interference for you. They can: list those that phoned, organize meals, e-mail or post info about your progress.

This only for the time that you need to heal, and get your bearings again. You will soon be back in the main stream of life. Your "village of supporters" will understand and respect your wishes.

"Those that bring sunshine to the lives of others cannot keep it from themselves."

James Barrie

Waiting:

When you were a child, "waiting" was associated with positive events. Your birthday, losing your first tooth, holidays... As you got older, you couldn't wait to drive, get a car, be called for a date, hear from colleges or jobs you applied for. Finally, you couldn't wait to get married, buy a home, to hold your beautiful baby in your arms. All these events had positive associations. HOW WONDERFUL WAITING WAS!

Unfortunately, there is the flip side of waiting. Waiting for potentially bad news. Waiting for information that you may not want to find out, but you must know. Waiting in THE WAITING ROOM.

Not only do you have to wait to talk about subjects you would rather not deal with, you are surrounded by people at different stages of their illnesses, which can be frightening. You see worried looks on the ill and their family members waiting with them.

There is an eerie silence in the waiting room of the oncologist. Few people engage in conversation. The clock seems to be at a standstill. Your wait can go well past an hour or two. Waiting in those circumstances can be exasperating, frustrating, and anxiety producing, especially when you know you are waiting for your blood to be drawn, or painful injections.

REMEMBER:

Managing this waiting takes an extra dosage of "patience". Expect the unexpected. Know there will be times things don't go the way you anticipated. Be grateful for the little things that are associated with waiting rooms; you get to shut your phone off, sit quietly and rest. You get to look at magazines you haven't gotten to read for lack of time or energy at home, or just daydream that one day soon you will no longer have to wait in the waiting room.

There is a different kind of waiting that is mentally terrifying; waiting for results from your medical test. Is your cancer in remission? Have your tumors shrunk? Are your markers in a better position?

Waiting to hear the results of these exams is one of the most stressful and anxiety producing times you can imagine. Each minute you wait feels like hours. Your imagination takes over.

REMEMBER:

Communicate to your doctor how difficult it is for you to wait. Ask if you can be accommodated in a more expeditious way. Tell him/her what time is best to call and which phone number to use. When you speak, it should be in an environment that offers privacy, especially if the conversation involves emotional discussions.

"When we have done our best, we should wait the result in peace. "

Sir John Lubbock

-RAY:

A diagnostic tool that can see through skin to look at growths or masses inside organs or skeletal muscles. With recent technological advancements, x-ray radiation is now used as a healing tool as well.

You will be introduced to a variety of x-rays and scans, with steps to follow to get a good reading, including food and clothing restrictions, medical beverages, or dye injections. Many x-ray machines have beds that pass through enclosed tunnels. If you have issues with being in enclosed areas, make sure to communicate with the personnel attending you.

REMEMBER:

You may receive radiation for a consecutive stretch of time, usually scheduled at the same time each day. You will see other patients on a daily basis, and bonds can form. The radiation waiting room can be a fascinating place for cancer does not discriminate, it can attack anyone. I had the privilege of forming relationships with other patients during my time at radiation, that would not have happened if we weren't all there at the same time

"It's a bird, it's a plane, it's superman!"

Superman - the one character I always admired for his super human strength and x-ray vision!

Y ESTERDAY:

Selective memory is a great commodity. When we think of our yesterdays, we tend to forget the hard times. No matter how you remember your yesterdays, there are innumerable lesson learned on your path. Through your experiences, you've gathered knowledge, coping mechanisms, and skills to propel you forward to help you face new life challenges.

REMEMBER:

Life is "Legoland"; everything you've done in the past is a building block to your present; your life experiences, people you've met, places you've visited, memories you've formed, lessons you've learned. All those skills are necessary to assist you in your survival.

You are on a journey. The scenery does change, nothing stays the same. You must find the path that will lead you successfully towards a healthier and happier tomorrow. Although your journey may be filled with pot holes and detours, if you use all that you have learned from other wise journeymen, you will have the strength to face your tomorrows.

"Yesterday, all my troubles seem so far away, now I long for yesterday"

The Beatles

Zero:

The beginning of the number line. For those with Leukemia, zero can bring good news or bad news. You learn, rather quickly, the significance of the number, and the meaning it holds in relation to your illness.

REMEMBER:

Zero carries two oppositional meanings.

The good meaning: with the number zero as the results of a pet/cat scan, you feel celebratory. Hearing you have zero evidence of cancer is fantastic news! You feel like shouting out in joy!

The bad meaning: zero white cells means a compromised immune system. You need medical intervention to increase your white blood cell count. You are at risk of infections. The white cells that act like soldiers are not there to protect your body.

No matter what zero you face, you will adapt to your challenges. With great news, you will appreciate the wonderful feeling of well being! You can resume living without your illness as a shadow. If you receive "zero" in respect to a compromised immune system, know that there are many excellent medical solutions that will help you be full functioning.

"Sometimes it is useful to know how big your zero is."

Unknown

As your personal guide, I hope you have learned useful facts to help make your journey down this bumpy path a smoother one.

We all know that life hands us challenges that can be huge, seemingly insurmountable. We have also learned that we are amazing in our ability to survive the most difficult times. We are resilient, we are strong, we can climb the highest mountains with a fierce sense of determination.

I know. During my last few years as a per-petual life student I have walked amongst many of you. You have provided me with the life les-sons that have made my journey successful..

Change can be frightening, but, upon reflec-tion, taking the risks I have had to take in order to be here today was well worth the price. I am eternally grateful to those individuals who sup-ported me, held me up when I was about to fall, brought my soul nourishment when I was starv-ing, and continue to cheer for me as I victoriously keep crossing new finish lines.

"If your experiences would benefit anybody, give them to someone."

Florence Nightingale

SUGGESTED READING MATERIAL

BOOKS THAT HELPED ME ON MY JOURNEY

- *A MUST READ: THE EMPOWERED PATIENT by Elizabeth Cohen, CNN Senior Medical Correspondent. The most well rounded book regarding how to navigate the health system. Includes how to locate updated information on the internet, how to ask the right questions and make the most out of your doctor's visit, how to understand your health insurance and fight back if your claims are denied, and how to purchase prescription drugs at the lowest cost. Power is Knowledge and Elizabeth Cohen certainly empowers you become your own advocate.*

- The Bible

- A Blessing in Disguise by Andrea Joy Cohen, M.D.

- The Book of Jewish Values - A Day to Day Guide to Ethical Living by Rabbi Joseph Telushkin

- Chemobrain, How Cancer Therapies Can Affect Your Mind...What Patients, Families and Doctors Need To Know by Ellen Clegg

- Chicken Soup for the Surviving Soul by Jack Canfield

- Chicken Soup for the Teacher's Soul by Jack Canfield and Mark Victor Hansen

- Chicken Soup for the Traveler's Soul by Jack Canfield, Mark Victor Hansen and Steve Zikman

- Heaven Can Wait - Surviving Cancer by Charlie Jones and Kim Doren

- Hot Chocolate for the Mystical Soul - 010 True Stories of Angels, Miracles, and Healings by Arielle Ford

- If I Live To Be 100 - Lessons From the Centenarians by Neenah Ellis

- In Lieu of Flowers...A Conversation for the Living by Nancy Cobb
- The Journey to Greatness...And How to Get There! by Noah BenShea
- Kitchen Table Wisdom by Rachel Naomi Remen
- The Last Lecture by Randy Pausch and Jeffrey Zaslow
- Life's Greatest Lessons, 20 Things That Matter by Hal Urban
- Livestrong by Lance Armstrong
- Love, Medicine and Miracles by Bernie Siegel, M.D.
- The Pocket Therapist - An Emotional Survival Kit by Therese J. Borchard
- Promise Me - How a Sister's Love Launched the Global Movement to End Breast Cancer by Nancy G. Brinker, Founder of SUSAN G. KOMEN FOR THE CURE with Joni Rodgers
- Simple Abundance by Sarah Ban Breathnach
- Small Miracles for the Jewish Heart by Yitta Halberstam
- The 10 Commandments of Common Sense by Hal Urban
- Too Soon Old, Too Late Smart...Thirty Things You Need To Know by Gordon Livingston,M.D., Foreword by Elizabeth Edwards
- The Total Cancer Wellness Guide - Reclaiming Your Life After Diagnosis by Kim Thiboldeaux, President and CEO and Mitch Golant, PhD., Vice President, Research and Development, The Wellness Community
- Waking Up, Fighting Back by Roberta Altman
- When Bad Things Happen to Good People by Harold S. Kushner
- The World According To Mister Rogers - Important Things to Remember by Fred Rogers
- Resilience - Reflections of the Burdens and Gifts of Facing Life's Adversities by Elizabeth Edwards

THE FOLLOWING BOOKS BROUGHT HUMOR INTO MY LIFE AND MADE ME SMILE

- Cosbyology - Essays and Observations from the Doctor of Comedy by Bill Cosby
- Matzo Balls for Breakfast and Memories of Growing Up Jewish by Alan King and Friends
- I Feel Bad About My Neck and Other Thoughts on Being a Woman by Nora Ephron
- A Collection of E-mails by Billie Jo Mouren and Gwen Andersen

THE FOLLOWING BOOK HELPED ME DREAM ABOUT MY FUTURE TRAVELS

- 1,000 Places To See Before You Die - A Traveler's Life List by Patricia Schultz

SPECIAL CHILDREN'S BOOKS

Children's literature touches your heart and makes you feel "warm and fuzzy." It also keeps you focused. Learn life lessons from children's literature, you are never too old to be read to!

- Small Talk - Wisdom from the Mouths of Babes by Anne Howard
- Pictures in the Fire - Text by Charles Lounsbury, Compiled by Harold Darling
- The Jester Has Lost His Jingle by David Saltzman
- Hope is an Open Heart by Lauren Thompson
- How Are You Peeling? by Jaime Curtis
- I Already Know I LOVE YOU by Billy Crystal

- I LOVE YOU FOREVER by Thomas Munch
- Sadako and the Thousand Paper Cranes by Eleanor Coerr
- The Giving Tree by Shel Silverstein
- Thank You, Mr. Falker by Patricia Polacco
- Something from Nothing by Phoebe Gilman
- Ira Says Goodbye by Bernard Waber
- Incredible You! - 10 Ways to let your Greatness Shine Through by Dr. Wayne W. Dyer with Kristina Tracy
- Crazy Hair Day by Barney Saltzberg
- Oh, The Places You'll Go! by Dr. Seuss
- The Little Engine That Could by Watty Piper and Loren Long

RECOMMENDED MAGAZINES

For the latest updates, research and education

- CURE   www.curetoday.com

To help you visualize your "Tomorrow's Travels"

- TRAVEL + LEISURE   www.travelandleisure.com
- CondeNast Traveler   www.cntraveler.com

To keep you inspired and informed with daily issues and book suggestions

- O Magazine by Oprah Winfrey

To learn the scoops about the famous, celebrate heroes among us, and let our imaginations run wild with the newest fashions...

- PEOPLE MAGAZINE   www.people.com

ACKNOWLEDGEMENTS

BEING ALWAYS THANKFUL,
GIVING GRATITUDE FROM MY HEART

To my Family, Friends, Doctors,
Forever Students and Parents,
and my Community of Supporters

I am forever thankful to my friends
Love poured from all your caring hearts,
offering me constant support, right from the start.

You came from close and afar. You all marched right in when I was feeling alone and frightened, lending me your ears and shoulders. You reassured me with words, hugs, and affirmations. You told me I would survive this challenge.

I am forever thankful for my village of helpers
When I was overwhelmed, you gave your time,
"Don't worry, we're here" you all cheerfully chimed.

When I was frustrated at my disabilities, you swept in like smiling Angels, stepping up to the plate, completing any task I requested. You were the most talented and tireless helpers. You were wedding coordinators, principals, teachers, parents, students, housecleaners, refrigerator organizers, drivers, e-mailers, tennis coaches and walkers.

I am forever thankful to my medical team

You stood by my side, with guidance and expertise,
 proving to me that great care really does exist.

My doctors, psychologists, technicians, nurses, and office receptionists... From the onset of my disease, you were by my side. You reassured me, saying I would be "just fine", that there are many options, we will fight your disease together, trying to help rid me of my worries.

I am forever thankful for my professional caretakers

You gave so much more than the services you render,
 your compassion and concern was loving and tender.

My massage therapist me with her healing hands, my most talented hair dresser, the chef who fed me equally with delicious food and his faithful blessings, the nail salon that gave me manicures and pedicures, the store personnel at my favorite shops... You did more for me than money could buy, you have been my forever cheerleaders.

I am forever thankful for my family, and their families

All around the world, you believed I would be okay,
I had so much to look forward to, so many reasons to stay.

My dear family saw me go from energetic, gregarious and strong, to suddenly too weak to walk. Through my ups and downs, you had faith in me, believing in my will to live. You were convinced that I would heal. You told me to visualize what I had to look forward to, including having grandchildren to play with. Your conviction gave me a reason to fight. I couldn't have made it without you.

I am forever thankful for the belief in this project
You worked so hard, I'm so grateful to you,
You've made my dreams of writing this book come true.

I prayed to be healthy and strong during this creative and emotional process, and to find the right words to bring help and hope to others. Destiny intervened; a literary agent crossed my path, listened and said I must write my story. A most amazing graphic artist/editor from Hawaii made my book shine. My talented photographer friend captured me "Still Breathing" next to a beautiful sunflower, reminding me and others to never take for granted the gifts the world has to offer. Together, we have written this book.

ABOUT THE AUTHOR

Michelle Pardes lives in Dana Point, California, with her husband Fred, her Shih Tzu dog Jake, and her Ragdoll cat Mittens. She shares her wisdom as a Survivorship Coach, speaking to individuals and groups, helping others cope with life threatening disease.

To learn more, contact Michelle, or to "pay forward" by sharing your own survivor story, visit:

www.stillbreathing.org